West African Nature Handbooks

General Editor: H. J. Savory, M.Sc.

SMALL MAMMALS OF WEST AFRICA

SMALL MAMMALS
OF WEST AFRICA

A. H. BOOTH

ILLUSTRATED BY CLIFFORD LEES

LONGMAN

LONGMAN GROUP LIMITED
London
*Associated companies, branches and representatives
throughout the world*

© **Longman Group Ltd. (formerly Longmans,
Green & Co. Ltd.) 1960**

*First published 1960
Third impression 1970*

ISBN 0 582 60848 1

PRINTED IN HONG KONG BY
SHECK WAH TONG PRINTING PRESS

CONTENTS

PLATES

FIGURES IN TEXT

INTRODUCTION

Assuming that most readers, like myself, do not read long introductions, a few explanatory sentences must suffice. The animals described are mammals, mainly small, but including a few big ones whose nearest relatives are small.

Most mammals, indeed most animals, frequent only certain types of vegetation. The main types of vegetation are roughly mapped in Fig. 1. There are plenty of books on vegetation. One of the best short accounts is Rosevear's in his *Checklist of Nigerian Mammals*, which is abundantly illustrated.

The descriptions have been cut down to a bare minimum, but supplemented by the illustrations they should be sufficient. With regard to size, if an animal is 'four inches long', that means that the tail is excluded, and there is usually a further remark about the length of the tail. Where possible, I have tried to indicate the animal's way of life. In many cases little is known, though much may be guessed.

For easy reference from the illustrations to the descriptions in the text, the names of the species illustrated have been printed in heavy type and numbered in the text. The same number is given in the Plates.

In writing this book I have used other books as little as possible. The result is a personal, but biased view of the fauna. Gaps will be obvious; on the other hand, in so short a book, gaps are inevitable, and they may as well be in one set of places as in another.

My particular thanks are due to Philip Mensah and Osumanie Moshi, who introduced me to West African mammals. My thanks are also due to my wife, who puts up with mammals around the house, and treats them as part of the family.

A.H.B.

OBITUARY

The reader will learn with sorrow of the sudden and tragic death of Angus Booth shortly after completing the manuscript of this delightful book.   He was originally appointed general editor of the series and planned himself to write a companion book on the larger mammals.   His untimely death at the early age of 30 not only stopped this work abruptly but robbed the world of a brilliant young man, already recognised as one of the leading authorities on the mammals of West Africa.

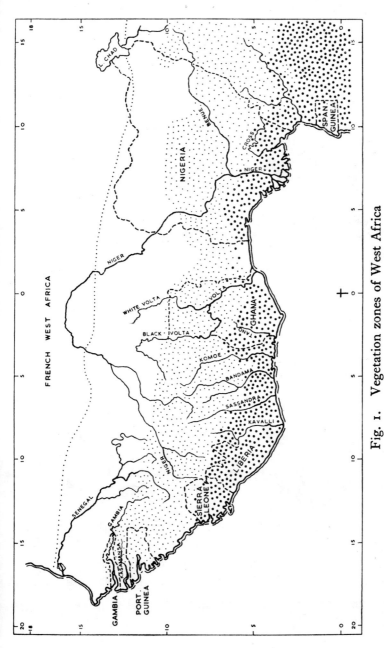

Fig. 1. Vegetation zones of West Africa

High Forest heavily dotted, Guinea Savannah lightly dotted, Sudan Savannah white; north of the dotted line are the semi-desert and desert zones.

a. Yellow-winged Bat

b. Leaf-nosed Bat

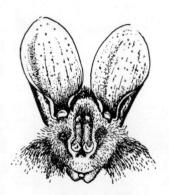

c. Slit-faced Bat

d. Horseshoe Bat

Fig. 2. Faces of some Insectivorous Bats

INSECTIVORA

Gathered together in the Insectivora are a group of lowly creatures which have little in common save that they have existed on earth unchanged for a very long time. Small brains, small eyes, a nocturnal life, and a diet largely consisting of insects—these are among their more important features, and zoologists believe that the earliest mammals on earth were something like this. There are three main groups in West Africa: the hedgehog, the musk shrews, and the otter shrew.

1. The West African Hedgehog   (*Plate I, 1*)
Erinaceus albiventris

There is really only one species of this creature though many have been described, and some may well be geographic races of it. The Hedgehog is only about six to eight inches long, stump-tailed, and covered in spines from the crown of the head to the haunches. The head, belly and limbs have a more normal covering of stiff hairs, white and full of fleas.

The spines are a means of defence. The animal can curl itself into a ball, so that they stick out in all directions and the head is entirely hidden. The only way of persuading it to uncurl then is to drop it in a bucket of water.

The Hedgehog lives in the savannah zones and in grassy areas generally. It is nocturnal and solitary. It eats insects, lizards, young snakes, eggs—in fact any animal food it can get. Two to four young are born at a time, and while they are babies their spines are soft, they cannot curl up, and their eyes are closed.

Hedgehogs very soon die if confined.

HEDGEHOG. *Mende:* seje. *Twi:* Fiampaakwa. *Ewe:* hlɔmade. *Dagbane:* yuyempini. *Igbo:* ɛbi nta. *Yoruba:* lili. *Hausa:* būshiya.

2. The Musk Shrews (*Plate I, 2*)

Crocidura spp.

Many kinds of Musk Shrew have been named from West Africa, but we have room for only a few. Shrews are mouse-like creatures, with small eyes, a very sharp nose, short, sleek fur, and, in the Musk-Shrews, a tail naked except for a few long, slender bristles. They are all nocturnal and very secretive in habits.

The Musk Shrews are so called because of their heavy, sickly-sweet smell. This is partly a defence mechanism, for most animals which hunt by smell will not touch them. Their main enemies are owls and snakes.

Giffard's Giant Shrew, *Crocidura giffardi*, is the largest West African species. Dull black in colour, it is at least six inches long without the tail, which adds another three inches. It lives only in the savannah zones.

The Common Musk Shrews of West Africa, *C. flavescenes* subspp., are distinctly smaller and lighter in colour. Similar in proportions to Giffard's Shrew, they attain about four and a half inches without the tail. They are the strongest smelling of all. The species is found in High Forest and in lighter woodland areas.

A true High Forest species is *C. poensis*, the Lesser Musk Shrew. This species is lighter in build, rather smaller (about three and a half inches), has a relatively longer tail (three inches), and olive-coloured fur.

All the shrews eat animal food, mainly insects, but in addition almost anything that they can overpower, such as small frogs, young lizards, earthworms, spiders, woodlice and so on. Though they are said also to feed on carrion, they are not always persuaded to do so in captivity.

SHREW. *Mende:* tuli. *Twi:* ofiam. *Ewe:* atʒe. *Dagbane:* nanteraya. *Igbo:* nk- akwə. *Yoruba:* asẹn. *Hausa:* jāɓa.

3. The Otter Shrew (*Plate I, 3*)

Potamogale velox

This is a giant among the Insectivora. More than that, it is one of those anatomical classics of which every zoologist has heard. When I first planned this book I intended to leave it out, for it was only known from the extreme east of Nigeria, from the Cross River eastwards. Now, however, news has come through that a similar creature has been found in French Guinea, and it may well turn up in other parts of West Africa.

About eleven inches long, with a nine-inch tail, it is covered in short, sleek fur, grey above and white below. The face is shrew-like, but the tip of the snout is somewhat flattened after the style of a duck's beak. The tail is also flattened, but in the opposite sense, being thicker from top to bottom than from side to side. The feet are broad.

The Otter Shrew lives in holes in the banks of streams and rivers, coming out by night to hunt in the water. It is said by some to feed exclusively upon crabs, by others to take fish and frogs. It is certainly a most expert swimmer, using the admirably-shaped tail to propel itself, rather than the feet.

It is hard to trap, and owing to its aquatic and nocturnal habits it is difficult to find out much about its way of life. Moreover it is one of those Cameroons mammals which have suffered from investigation by romantic, rather than by strictly accurate naturalists. As a result, even the little that we do know is clouded by uncertainty. This is a pity, but resident naturalists could do much to clear up the facts, and really accurate observations would be most welcome.

3

CHIROPTERA, OR BATS

Probably more than a hundred different kinds of Bat have been described from West Africa. This fact, coupled with their unfamiliarity to most people, makes the task of selection difficult indeed.

Bats are the only mammals which truly fly. The forelimb is a wing, as it is in the birds, but it is very different in structure and appearance. It is a delicate membrane of skin, stretched between the long, slender fingers. The hind limb, by contrast, is almost useless for locomotion, and can be used only in a shuffling crawl, or as a hook, by which the bat suspends itself upside down at rest.

There are two main groups: Fruit Bats and Insectivorous Bats. They may easily be distinguished in the hand, often by ear, and more rarely in flight. The Fruit Bats are as a group far larger animals. The face of a Fruit Bat is rather dog-like, unadorned save that in the males of some species the lips may be much wrinkled. Insectivorous Bats often have quite revolting faces, with excessively large ears and thin outgrowths of skin, variously ornamented, in the nose and ear regions. The eyes of Fruit Bats are of normal size, those of Insectivorous Bats generally very small. If these characters fail to distinguish the bat in the hand, the teeth and tail are a sure guide. Fruit Bats have simple cheek-teeth, while those of Insectivorous Bats are complex. The tail of Fruit Bats is tiny, while that of Insec-

---

BAT. *Mende:* dava. *Twi:* ampan. *Ewe:* awoe. *Dagbane:* gyɛnkpiberega. *Igbo:* ese. *Yoruba:* adan. *Hausa:* jēmāge.
Particular species.—*M.:* taja (*fruit*), tɔka. *T.:* ɔdankwansere (*eidolon*), apantweaa (*hypsignathus*), hwenekron (*hipposideros*), ahwerede (*pipistrelles*). *D.:* zɔŋ (*fruit*), zunzɔŋ. *H.:* dalangashi (*fruit*), birbiri, dwādwa, kurwa, ƙyami, makēri.

4

tivorous Bats is connected to the legs by a membrane (here called the 'tail membrane') which has a large area, and looks just like part of the wing membrane. It helps the bat in flight, and may even be used for catching the prey.

All Bats have but a single pair of teats in the female, and only a single young is normally produced each year. The baby is carried about by the mother in flight, clinging to the breast.

FRUIT BATS

4. The Straw-coloured Fruit Bat   (*Plate II, 4*)

Eidolon helvum

This is the largest of West African bats. It has a length of eight or nine inches, and a span of up to two and a half feet. The name sufficiently describes the colour.

Found right from the Sudan Savannah to the coast, the Straw-coloured Fruit Bat goes about in large flocks and migrates seasonally over great distances in search of abundant food. In some areas, for example, it is rarely seen except when the Silk Cotton tree is in flower. For it feeds not only on fruits but also on flowers, probably visiting the latter in the first place for the nectar, but staying to eat quantities of pollen and the flowers themselves. The twittering and shrieking of a feeding flock is unbearable at close quarters.

This bat probably has few effective enemies. Only the man with the gun can make any appreciable reduction in their numbers. As they hang like so many fruits in some lofty tree, they can be brought down a dozen at a time by a charge of small bird-shot. To what purpose? They are roughly skinned, smoked, and then strung on sticks for sale in the market. One's impression of this delicacy is of rows of grinning teeth set at all angles, for the heads are left on the bodies in the market.

Most Fruit Bats can be kept in captivity. They do not need room to fly, and are content to make crawling down to feed their only daily exercise. Indian Fruit Bats have even bred under these conditions.

5. The Rosette Bats (*Plate II, 5*)

Rousettus smithi and *Rousettus aegyptiacus*

These Fruit Bats are rather exceptional among West African species, in that they seek dark places to hide. Most of our Fruit Bats are content to rest during the day among shady leaves.

They are only moderate-sized Fruit Bats, Smith's Rosette being about four inches, and the Egyptian Rosette about five inches long. The males wear, high up on the chest, a rosette-like whorl of fur on either side. This is absent in the female.

Smith's Rosette is a fawn colour, often with contrasting shades on the head and back, rendering it almost handsome. It is a High Forest species, so far known only from the Niger westward, though a related form is found in more easterly areas. It lives in hollow trees, in colonies of about a dozen. It seems to favour the drier parts of the High Forest zone. The young are born in August.

The Egyptian Rosette is found all over tropical Africa and even beyond. Comparatively few have been collected in West Africa, but it apparently occurs in both forest and savannah, and normally lives in caves. I have found colonies of up to fifteen individuals, though there always seems to be room for many more. It is a much more sombre bat than Smith's Rosette, some shade of dark brown all over, and without the contrasting head colour.

The only cry I have ever heard from either species is a nondescript twittering.

6. The Gambian Fruit Bat (*Plate II, 6*)

Epomophorus gambianus

This bat belonging to the 'Epaulet-bat' group, is found in savannah, and occasionally in High Forest, throughout West Africa. It is fairly large—about six inches long, with a wingspan of over two feet. The fur may be almost any shade of fawn or light brown, with a little tuft of pure white at the base of each ear. The naked wing membranes and ears are tinged with yellow. The male differs from the female in the head and shoulder region. The head is much longer and the lips more wrinkled. There is also a tuft of white hairs, the 'epaulets', in an eversible pocket on each shoulder.

Colonies of the Gambian Fruit Bat are generally much smaller than the flocks of the Straw-coloured Fruit Bat. A roost may contain up to fifty in a favourite tree such as the Senegal Mahogany. Many specimens, particularly males, are scattered singly. At dusk, or slightly before, the males set up a shrill piping in single notes, rather like a high-pitched (and cracked) bell. While it utters this cry, the animal has the white epaulet fully exposed, and the wings are vibrated rapidly. The significance of the whole performance is presumably sexual.

The food of this species includes a variety of fruits and flowers, according to the season of the year. Various species of wild fig are an unfailing attraction. Sometimes the food is eaten on the spot, but frequently the bat will stuff its mouth and cheeks with food, and then fly off to a convenient perch to chew and swallow the mouthful.

Though local migrations are frequent, it is not thought that there is any mass migration such as that performed by the Straw-coloured Fruit Bat, or that distances of more than a very few miles are involved.

There are many other Fruit Bats in West Africa, mostly belonging to the Epaulet group, but we have not room to give more than a few notes on the commoner ones.

7. The Hammer-headed Bat   (*Plate II, 7*)

Hypsignatus monstrosus

This animal, or more accurately, the male of this species, contends strongly for the title 'ugliest mammal in the world'. Though it is but an enlarged version of the Gambian Fruit Bat, its enormous snout and wrinkled lips are truly horrific. The female is quite normal in appearance. This is the second

7

largest West African bat. It lives in the High Forest and is not so gregarious as the Gambian Fruit Bat. Its call, presumably uttered only by the male, is 'geg geg geg gegegegeg', and resembles that of many of the forest frogs.

Also a High Forest species is the noisy Franquet's Fruit Bat, *Epomops franqueti*. A little larger than the Gambian Fruit Bat, it is difficult to distinguish from it, except by its shorter face and even more raucous piping. This is the true High Forest Fruit Bat of medium size. The Gambian Fruit Bat is an interloper which has come in with the extensive clearings made by cultivation, and really belongs in the savannah.

There are two common Dwarf Epaulet Bats, one a forest form, *Nanonycteris veldkampi*, which is rather short-faced like *Epomops*. The other is *Micropteropus pusillus*, which is a longer-faced savannah form, resembling *Epomophorus*. Both are only about three inches long, with a wingspan of a little over a foot. They feed on fruits and flowers.

TOMB BATS

Taphozous spp.

With the Tomb Bats we pass from the Fruit Bats to the Insectivorous Bats. And of all the latter, the Tomb Bats are among the most 'normal' in appearance. The eyes are not greatly reduced, and they have little of the bizarre facial 'ornamentation' which makes most of the Insectivorous Bats so hideous. The tail is rather loosely carried in the tail membrane, projecting somewhat above it. I shall describe only two Tomb Bats.

The Mauritius Tomb Bat, *Taphozous mauritianus*, is almost beautiful. About three inches long, it has soft, thick silvery grey fur on the back, and almost white wings. It is found throughout West Africa. It roosts single or in small colonies, generally in crevices, into which it crawls with great agility. A favourite place is among the bases of palm fronds.

Plate I

Scale
0   1   2   3 ins.

1   West African Hedgehog
2   Musk Shrew
3   Otter Shrew

Plate II

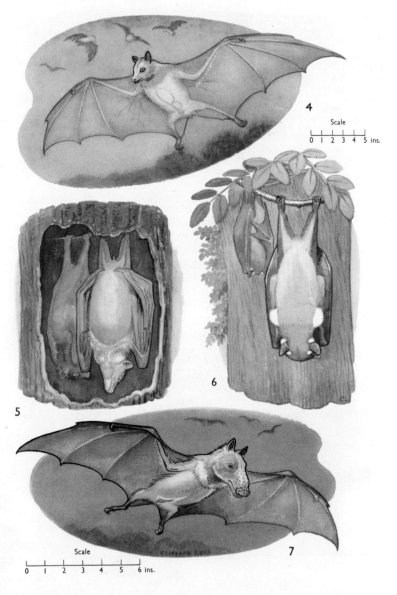

Scale

0 1 2 3 4 5 ins.

Scale

0 1 2 3 4 5 6 ins.

CLIFFORD LEES

4   Straw-coloured Fruit Bat   6   Gambian Fruit Bat

5   Rosette Bats   7   Hammer-headed Bat

Plate III

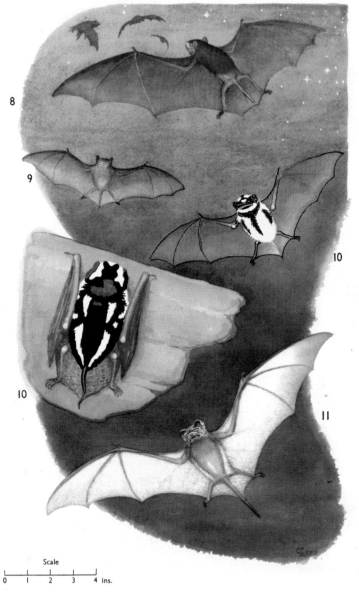

8   Pel's Pouched Bat

9   Pipistrelle

10   Butterfly Bats

11   Lesser Free-tailed Bat

Plate IV

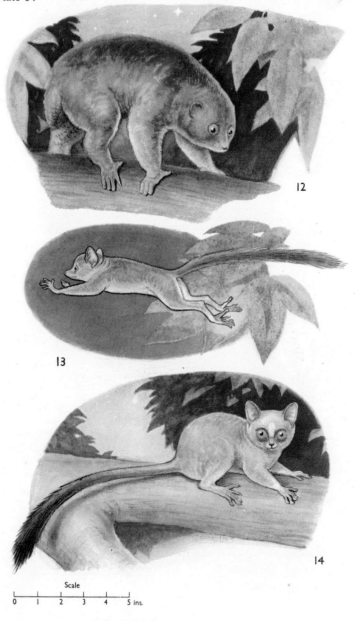

Scale

0   1   2   3   4   5 ins.

12   Bosman's Potto

13   Demidoff's Galago, or the lesser Bush Baby

14   Senegal Galago

8. Pel's Pouched Bat *(Plate III, 8)*

Taphozous peli

This is a much larger bat of the High Forest from Liberia eastward. About the size of a Rosette Bat, it is dark brown all over. The fur is close and oily in texture. The 'pouch' is at the base of the throat, and contains a gland. We do not know the significance of this pouch, but it occurs in many Tomb Bats.

Even a novice can recognise this bat in flight. It comes out at sunset, while there is still plenty of light, flying over the forest both swiftly and at a great height. As dusk deepens, it comes lower and lower, until it only just skims the roads and the bushes in the clearings which are a favourite hunting ground. As it flies, it utters a series of almost mechanical clicks. After about 8 p.m. one sees or hears nothing more of it till nearly dawn next day.

SLIT-FACED BATS

Nycteris spp.

This is one of the most varied of all the groups of African bats. There are many species in West Africa, but except in size they are all remarkably alike. The ears are always very long, the eyes minute, the face has a distinct groove running up the snout, with membranous 'lips' on either side of it (Fig. 2c). The tail is about the same length as the body, from one and a half to three inches according to species. It is very slender, and lies entirely enclosed within the tail membrane. The colour is generally some shade of grey-brown or red-brown, the fur long and sparse, the hairs paler at the base than at the tip.

Most of the species of Slit-faced Bat live in hollow trees, all of them in dark holes of some sort. A favourite man-made roost is provided by culverts under roads and railways. Some species are gregarious, forming colonies of up to twenty strong, others live single or in pairs.

9

The Hairy Slit-faced Bat, *Nycteris hispida*, is the only one I will mention by name, because probably everyone in West Africa, whether he knows it or not, has seen it. It lives in all types of country, and commonly flies into houses. Despite its small size (it is only about four inches long altogether), its flight is strong. Great use is made of the tail membrane, especially when turning a corner or when changing from level flight to a dive or a climb. If the bat is trapped inside a room, one notices that during flight it makes a continuous noise which sounds rather like a watch being wound up. All Insectivorous Bats are thought to make noises like this, but they are only audible at close quarters. They also make noises which are quite inaudible to the human ear, but which have been recorded electrically.

The Yellow-winged Bat, *Lavia frons*. This astonishing bat looks like one of the Slit-faced Bats 'exaggerated'. The ears are enormously long (two-inch ears on a three-inch bat!), and are joined together above the forehead. There is a huge 'tragus', an extra lobe pointing upward just in front of the ear. This is present in many bats, but nowhere else to this extent. The nose bears two tall, pointed growths, corresponding to the 'lips' of the 'slit' in the Slit-faced Bats. The eyes are rather large for a bat. The tail is forked, though contained within the membrane. Finally, the wings are a bright orange-yellow colour, as are the ears and all the naked areas of skin. The fur may be orange-yellow also, but is often a rather dull grey (Fig. 2a).

Remarkable in appearance, these bats are no less so in habits. They are often to be seen hunting by day. Their roosting-places are far from dark: indeed, they seem to be even less particular in this respect than the Epaulet Bats. I have seen a pair hanging in a bush which was almost bare of leaves, practically unshaded from the glaring heat of the dry season. Nevertheless, their colour and position were such that they looked from a distance just like a pair of dead leaves.

10

The Yellow-winged Bat is very strong on the wing. Though I have never observed such an incident, it is reported that among other things it will even overpower and eat small bats.

Members of this family of bats are said to bear twins quite frequently. The only three pregnant females I have examined each had a single embryo. It would seem that the young are born in about February, a common breeding season for the smaller West Coast bats.

HORSESHOE BATS
Rhinolophus spp.

Many different kinds of Horseshoe Bat have been reported from West Africa. All of them are rather small. Their chief distinguishing feature is the shape of the 'nose-leaf', the growth of skin in the snout region. The lower part of this organ is shaped exactly like a horseshoe (Fig. 2d).

West African Horseshoe Bats are normally cave- or hollow tree-dwellers. Their flight is rather weak and slow, which makes them one of the few Insectivorous Bats which are fairly easy to 'bag' on the wing.

LEAF-NOSED BATS
Hipposideros spp.

This is another big group, mainly of forest bats. It is particularly important and abundant in West Africa. Leaf-nosed Bats are rather like Horseshoe Bats in general appearance, but the nose-leaf does not have quite the same shape. In both groups, however, the broad ear is pointed at the tip. The males of most species have a curious gland on the forehead, which produces a musky substance (Fig. 2b). In size, they range from the two-inch *Hipposideros beatus* to the five-inch *H. commersoni.*

H. beatus, the Dwarf Leaf-nosed Bat, may live in large colonies in roofs in the High Forest zone. It is a terrible lodger to have upstairs, on account of the smell of the droppings. It breeds in February and March, and this is the time to exterminate it, for the gravid and carrying females are rather slow in flight at this season. It is dark brown.

H. caffer, the African Leaf-nosed Bat, is a very common forest and savannah form, about two and a half inches long, living in hollow trees in small numbers or in caves or roofs in big colonies. It may be red-brown, orange or grey-brown.

H. cyclops, the Grizzled Leaf-nosed Bat, is very ugly. Its grizzled grey, woolly fur and outsize head give it a very 'lumpy' appearance. It smells fouler than most. It lives in big hollow trees, in groups of up to a dozen, often in company with Dormice, Flying Squirrels and other creatures.

H. commersoni, the Giant Leaf-nosed Bat, is the largest *Hipposideros*. Red or yellow in colour, and with a wingspan of two and a half feet, it is indeed a notable animal. It lives in colonies in huge hollow trees or solitary in suitable foliage. It also breeds in February.

PIPISTRELLES AND OTHERS
Vespertilionidae

This 'Family' of Bats is really a huge group of varied types, which might be called the 'ordinary bats'. I can really only pick out a few of the less ordinary forms which might be recognisable on first sight.

9. The Pipistrelles   (*Plate III, 9*)

Pipistrellus spp.

These are among the commonest and smallest of the world's mammals. Some of them are only an inch long without the tail, and weigh as little as a gramme. If that doesn't convey very much, think of a heap of sixty thousand of these bats. That would be the weight of an average man! These bats are common in thatched roofs, or in crevices in vegetation. The base of a banana leaf is a frequent hiding place. During the day they are very torpid, and may be picked up in the hand, a rare feature in West African bats. They have a shrill squeak when handled, and, like all bats, *very* sharp teeth.

10. Butterfly Bats   (*Plate III, 10*)

Glauconycteris

We do not often think of bats as beautiful, but the Butterfly Bats, *Glauconycteris* spp., must certainly be admitted to approach it. *G. superba* (it hasn't a common name) is really quite exceptional. Boldly patterned in pure black and snowy white, it has only once been collected in West Africa, and must be accounted a great prize. It is a forest species.

A bat which commonly enters houses in the savannah zones is the Yellow Bat, *Scotophilus nigrita*. It is one of the biggest house-haunting bats, and is conspicuous for its yellow body and nearly black wings.

FREE-TAILED BATS

Tadarida spp.

The Germans call bats 'flying mice'. The Free-tailed Bats are those which perhaps most nearly deserve the name. The tail membrane is rather small, and the thick tail projects well beyond it. Though the lips and ears are somewhat wrinkled, the general appearance is much more 'normal' than in some groups we have met. Most of the species are of moderate size, two and a half to three inches in length, brown in colour, the wings long and narrow and very pale. There are sometimes white patches on the belly, and strips of white fur just below the 'armpit'.

11. The Lesser Free-tailed Bat   (*Plate III, 11*)

Tadarida pumila

Most of the Free-tailed Bats are savannah forms, though a few live in the High Forest. The Lesser Free-tailed Bat, frequently occupies roofs, greatly to the distress of the occupant of the house chosen. Enormous numbers are often to be found in corrugated metal roofs in the savannah zones, and very noisy and noisome they are.

Free-tailed Bats do not, and probably cannot, hang upside down from a perch. Their broad feet are used for scrabbling into crevices, and quite a rapid form of locomotion can be achieved with feet and folded wings. Their departure to hunt just about sunset and their return at any time of night, but more particularly at about 5.30 a.m., is marked by great outbursts of twittering, shuffling and, one suspects, a mild form of fighting for precedence. Even in the daytime, they have a tendency to wake up and adjust position quite frequently— not surprising when one considers the temperature of a tin roof in the midday heat.

This last point is a most interesting and unusual one. Mammals usually live, certainly rest in places which are cooler than the temperature of their own bodies. These Bats often choose resting-places which would appear to be warmer than their own internal temperature.

PRIMATES

This is the group, or Order of mammals to which Man belongs. All the West African Primates have a number of characters in common with Man, which it may be of interest to point out. Their eyes look directly forward, their brains are relatively large, and they have nails, not claws, on most, if not all of the fingers and toes. Both hand and foot are capable of truly grasping objects (compare a dog or a cow in this respect). Not only are the digits very flexible, but the thumb (where present) and the first toe are 'opposable'. This means that they can be moved widely away from the other digits and curled round an object, as when we grasp a hammer.

The Primates have very keen eyes and ears, but generally a poor sense of smell. They are for the most part very active creatures, and live at least partly in trees. Most other animals, except birds, have comparatively poor eyesight and a very good sense of smell.

Primates produce very few young at a time, only one or two in all West African forms. All species are also, for their size, slow to come to maturity.

LOWER PRIMATES

The lower Primates of West Africa include the Bush Babies or Galagos, and the Pottos. We call them 'lower' because many of the characters which are developed in Man, Apes and Monkeys are here found only in a rudimentary state. All are nocturnal, with large, prominent eyes. There is a pointed snout, with a wet muzzle like a dog's. The teeth are sharp, especially the front ones. In fact, they are in some ways more like a Hedgehog's than a Monkey's teeth. They take a good deal of animal food, especially insects. Their ears are prominent, delicate and hairless. Like most mammals, they do not distinguish colours, except as shades of grey.

12. Bosman's Potto   *(Plate IV, 12)*

Perodicticus potto

This is one of the strangest animals in Africa. It is the size of a small cat, with brown woolly fur and a short, apparently useless tail. It is certainly a Primate, but Primates are generally active creatures, and here is one which is as slow and deliberate in its movements as a chameleon. It has long legs, and hands and feet of remarkable breadth and grasping power: indeed, the index finger is reduced to a mere stump, giving it an even greater grasping span than a complete hand would possess.

The eyes are large, as is often the case in nocturnal animals. Unlike a monkey, the Potto always takes time to turn his head to look at something—a sideways glance is insufficient for his cautious nature.

The Potto is a forest-dweller. He moves slowly about at night, for the most part taking animal food, the unwary insect, a gecko or a snail, but does not neglect fruits should they appear in front of his nose. The day he spends curled up asleep in dense foliage. In this position, another of his peculiarities can be observed. The bones of the neck have extensions which project upwards just beneath the skin, forming a little row of blunt spikes. An enemy coming upon a Potto curled up (his defensive, as well as his sleeping posture) would naturally attempt to seize it by the neck. It is said that the Potto then jerks his head back, catching some tender portion of his assailant—lips, tongue or nose—between the spikes. If this is true, the wound would certainly be painful.

One or two young are born at a time. Young pottos are attractive pets, despite their almost constant grumbling. But handle with care!

Plate V

Scale

0   1   2   3 ft.

15   Red Colobus Monkey   17   Black Colobus Monkey

16   Olive Colobus Monkey   18   Green Monkey

Plate VI

Scale

0   1   2   3 ft.

19 Mona Monkey   22 Putty-nosed Monkey

20 Diana Monkey   23 Red Patas Monkey

21 Spot-nosed Monkey

13. Demidoff's Galago, or the Lesser Bush Baby

Galagoides demidovii (*Plate IV, 13*)

Though a relative of the Potto, the Lesser Bush Baby is a complete contrast in disposition and behaviour. The large eyes (here much emphasised), naked ears (much larger and more sensitive), pointed nose, grasping hands and feet, even the yellow tinge to the naked areas of skin, are all basically the same as in the Potto. But this is a tiny creature, about a quarter of a pound in weight, a foot long, but over half the length taken up by the elegant bushy tail. It may be any colour from red-brown to olive-grey, with lighter under-parts. Sometimes we find pure cream-coloured specimens. The fur is soft and thick, very pleasant to touch.

Lesser Bush Babies may lead a solitary or a family life in the daytime, curled up asleep in a tiny nest of fresh leaves, generally placed in a thick bush. At night they are all activity. They run about the branches of the lower forest trees and jump astonishing distances in any direction except backwards. The very long hind legs, and especially ankle bones, are obviously the secret of this performance.

The food in the wild state is almost entirely insects. In captivity, however, they will readily take fruit and milk. The most pleasing and convenient way to keep Bush Babies is in a chicken-wire cage on a verandah. A light placed above the cage will attract insects, some of which will find their way into the cage and thence into the Bush Baby's stomach. A small sleeping-box should be put inside the cage.

Either one or two young are born at a time. The youngsters are very easily tamed, indeed they have no fear.

Bush Babies have quite a vocabulary. Their loudest call is a high-pitched 'ti-ti-ti' going on for many syllables, and rising to a crescendo.

14. The Senegal Galago (*Plate IV, 14*)

Galago senegalensis

This is the Galago of the savannah zones. It is like the Lesser Bush Baby in appearance and proportions, but is larger, and has a grey, woolly coat. It is about eighteen inches long including the tail.

Though it does not have the suddenness of movement which we see in the smaller species, it is nevertheless a very active creature, and subsists largely on insects, which it catches in its hands. It is also said to take fruit.

The Senegal Galago probably prefers to spend the day in hollow trees, but where these are not available it will rest in dense foliage. It is most abundant where the trees are sufficiently close together to allow it to jump from one to the next. On the other hand, it does not normally enter forest patches in the Guinea Savannah, preferring the more open trees of the 'orchard bush', which normally have grass beneath them. In marginal areas on the edge of the High Forest zone, one can shine a light towards the savannah and see reflected the eyes of the Senegal Galago, then turn round and see the eyes of the Lesser Bush Baby blinking in the forest.

Twins seem if anything to be the rule in the Senegal Galago. There are in fact two pairs of teats in the female, as is commonly the case in the Lower Primates.

There are three other species of Lower Primate in West African High Forest: two Galagos and a Potto. But they are restricted to the extreme east of Nigeria.

MONKEYS

The Monkeys, Apes, and Man are generally considered to be much more 'advanced' creatures than those just described. In what ways we shall see.

Most people have the idea that monkeys go about the forest in troops, eating fruit and nuts, making an enormous noise and swinging from branches by their tails. The first is accurate, the second and third only sometimes true, and the fourth, at any rate in the Old World, a downright myth. We have about fifteen species of Monkey in West Africa, most of them split up into quite distinct geographic races. Each species has a definite part to play in the life of forest or savannah. They differ in the food they eat, in the height from the ground at which they feed and sleep, and in many other ways.

All monkeys feed by day and sleep by night. Their food is either fruits or leaves, sometimes both. Thanks to their excellent eyesight, complete with colour vision, they can distinguish the ripest or most succulent food from a distance. In one other respect their eyes, like ours, are superior to those of all other mammals including the Lower Primates: they are stereoscopic. This means that not only do they look directly forward, but they are so interconnected within the brain that they can judge distances and see things in 'depth'. The ability to judge distances is just one of those gifts which we rarely appreciate, but next time you have a bad eye, you may notice that even in an

---

MONKEY. *Mende:* kwala. *Twi:* nkyeneboa. *Ewe:* kese. *Dagbane:* (see below). *Igbo:* ɛnwɛ. *Yoruba:* ǫbǫ. *Hausa:* biri.
    Particular species—*M.:* nguwa (*red colobus*), kpeŋgbaa (*olive colobus*), njaguaa (*green*), towaa (*black colobus*), Iǝgbǝ (*mona*), keli, hokpalakuli. *T.:* ɛbene (*red colobus*), asibe (*olive colobus*), ɛfoǝ (*black colobus*), akakawa (*green*), kwakuo (*mona*), boapea (*diana*), ahwenhema (*spot-nosed*), asabara (*red patas*), eku (*mangabey*). *E.:* tǝfie (*olive colobus*), ŋkume yibǝǝ (*green*), atakpa (*black colobus*), fie (*mona*), fiesrʒe (*spot-nosed*), abladzɛɛ (*red patas*). *D.:* gyaŋa (*green*), ŋmansulega (*black*). *Y.:* awere (*red colobus*), ǫdan orokun (*black colobus*), ewere (*diana*), ijimere (*red patas*). *H.:* atala, gāta, dūje, māne, tsūla, ƙirƙa.

everyday action like picking up a tea-cup you are liable to make a clumsy mess. In fact, much of our everyday work depends on the ability to co-ordinate eye and hand. This is very important for a monkey also, not only in feeding, but also in leaping about the branches.

Monkeys probably do not reproduce till they are at least five years old, and even then they have at most one infant each year, or very rarely twins.

THE COLOBUS MONKEYS

'Colobus' is a Greek word meaning 'maimed'. These monkeys are so called because the thumb is much reduced. In fact, this is no great handicap, for they are all leaf-eaters. All they have to do is to extend their four long fingers and haul the nearest leafy twig to their mouths. They have no cheek-pouches to store the food, but they do have a complicated stomach to help them digest it.

15. The Red Colobus Monkey   (*Plate IV, 15*)

Procolobus badius

Four races of this beautiful monkey occur in West Africa, curiously enough one in each of the British Commonwealth territories. All are fairly large monkeys, about twelve to twenty pounds in weight, with short, red and black fur. The red colour is mainly on the limbs and belly, the black on the back and head. The Sierra Leone and Ghana races are the most beautiful, with deep red and jet black coloration.

The Red Colobus is restricted to the taller mature High Forest (except in the Gambia), and is absent between mid-Ghana and the Cross River in Nigeria. They live in large troops, often of up to fifty monkeys. Their ability to leap is quite unrivalled, and most spectacular jumps are made from one tall tree to the next. A troop of Red Colobus is rarely silent. Their high-pitched 'kyow', a very bird-like sound, betrays even a resting troop. Moreover, their behaviour when hunted by Man is far from cunning. Hence these harmless and beautiful creatures are in danger of becoming extinct.

The young are considered impossible to rear in captivity.

16. The Olive Colobus Monkey (*Plate V, 16*)

Procolobus versus

This is the smallest of the Colobus Monkeys, only eight or nine pounds in weight, and at first sight very dull and ordinary-looking. A reddish back merges with olive-green flanks and grey under-parts. The only ornamentation is a little crest of upright hairs on the crown. But if you examine the fur closely, you will see that it has most beautiful, subtle tints.

The Olive Colobus is found from Sierra Leone to Togoland. It is far from rare, though it is both shy and silent, and few people can claim to be really familiar with it. It lives a retiring life in thickets in the High Forest and fringing forest. The small family parties are often found feeding close to the ground in company with Spot-nosed or Mona Monkeys. The more inquisitive fruit-eaters give the alarm when they spot an enemy, and the Olive Colobus takes heed, abandons its meal of leaves, and either slips away quietly or conceals itself in dense foliage. I have been within six feet of a full-grown Olive Colobus curled up like a Potto, imagining itself to be invisible.

The voice is alto in pitch, like that of the Red Colobus. If anything, the Olive Colobus's record in captivity is even worse than that of the Red. The babies are carried in the mouth of the mother, and it is said that when the mother is shot, she bites the youngster. Hence they are rarely obtained. The young baby seems unable to cling to the mother's very short fur, partly no doubt owing to the lack of a thumb, partly because of the tangled thickets that the animal frequents. But older offspring are able to cling beneath the mother's belly in the usual way.

21

17. The Black Colobus Monkey (*Plate V, 17*)

Colobus polykomos

The most widely ranging, commonest, largest and most handsome of the Colobus Monkeys are the Black Colobus. They are up to twenty-five pounds in weight, the males being larger than the females. In the western species, *C. polykomos*, the entire body is jet black, with long fur over the back and shoulders. There is white fur round the face, and in the most easterly race on the thighs as well. The Cameroons species, *C. abyssinicus*, also has beautiful long white hairs on the shoulders and flanks. All these monkeys have long white tails.

Though typical of the High Forest zone, Black Colobus range far into the Guinea Savannah along river banks and in patches of dry forest.

Where there are no Red Colobus, the Black Colobus lives and feeds in any layer of the forest, though apparently avoiding thickets, and hence rare in secondary bush. In the presence of the Red Colobus, it tends to feed in the middle layers, leaving the topmost branches to the Red Colobus. Troops may be of any size, up to forty or fifty strong. Unlike the other Colobus Monkeys, this species has a high level of troop organisation, a large male being the leader, and exerting his authority both vocally and physically. The full cry of the male is a deep 'rurr-rurr-rurr' many times repeated.

In West Africa, Black Colobus Monkeys are not difficult to keep in captivity. Milk and leaves are a complete diet for the youngsters. Beware of giving them fruit, which they will eat, but which is bad for their digestion. They are friendly and intelligent pets.

The Black Colobus is persecuted for meat and skins more than any other monkey. If it is not protected, it will soon become a very rare animal.

18. The Green Monkey (*Plate V, 18*)

Cercopithecus aethiops

'Just an ordinary monkey . . . sort of greyish.' That is how people often describe their pet monkeys to me. And usually the animal in question is the Green Monkey. Speckled grey-green above, cream below, with a black face and no particular distinguishing marks, its only ornament is its side-whiskers. These are either directed back and up (*C.a. tantalus*, the Nigerian form) or else give a curious half-moon effect (*C.a. sabaeus*, the western form). In fine specimens there is also a curious little tuft of whitish hairs on either side of the root of the tail, which project from the line of the body. Green Monkeys weigh from six to fourteen pounds.

The Green Monkey is an animal of the Guinea and Sudan Savannahs, favouring dry forest along watercourses (in contrast to the Red Patas, which keeps to more open ground). It comes to the ground frequently, and its dull coloration doubtless affords it some protection in the dry grasses. Where not kept down, it may become a serious agricultural pest, like all savannah monkeys.

Troops are not normally very large, though seasonally they may become so, especially when food is short. Larger aggregations are said to be commoner in the Sudan than in the Guinea Savannah. Compared to High Forest species, they are rather silent monkeys; the harsh 'kek-kek-kek' of the male is the cry most frequently heard. The species is entirely frugivorous, sometimes taking even grass seeds.

They are the easiest monkeys to keep in captivity, for they can tolerate a monotonous diet. Males very often become dangerous as they grow, and should not be allowed near children.

19. The Mona Monkey   (Plate VI, 19)

Cercopithecus mona and *Cercopithecus campbelli*

The Mona Monkeys, of which there are several different kinds in West Africa, are in captivity quite the liveliest, most charming and most affectionate of all. Brightly coloured when healthy, they are distinguished from all other *Cercopithecus* monkeys by their pink, flesh-coloured lips. In the True Mona, found from the Cameroons to Ghana, the back is a warm red-brown, and there are white spots at the root of the tail on either side. In Campbell's Mona, there are no rump-spots, and the back is a golden-green. Campbell's Mona occurs from Ghana to Sierra Leone, a different race in each territory.

Mona Monkeys are at home in the middle and lower layers of the High Forest, where they live almost entirely on wild fruits. When undisturbed, they are very active and vocal. They often give the alarm to more stolid and unobservant creatures when an enemy is near. Their vocabulary is probably more varied than that of any other West African species. Even the bark of the male, normally a very constant specific feature, is variable: it may be 'wă-hu', 'wĕ-hu', 'wŏ-hu', or just 'wĕ'. Some of the more intimate calls are very musical. There is also a curious booming call, like a ship's siren. This has been attributed by some people to the Giant Forest Squirrel, but it is actually made by the Mona.

Troops of about a dozen or so are normal in mature forest, but in and near cultivated areas, many more band together. Though not so widespread as the Spot-nosed Monkey, the Mona in Ghana follows fringing forest along river banks far into the Guinea Savannah.

The Mona is quite a small monkey, eight to twelve pounds is a normal male weight, six to nine pounds for the females.

20. The Diana Monkey (*Plate VI, 20*)

Cercopithecus diana

This is without question the most beautiful of all West African monkeys. There are two races, both confined to the forest between the Volta River and Sierra Leone. The colours are black, white, red and some shade of orange. The artist's picture shows the eastern race, *C.d. roloway*. But you can recognise either race at a glance by the *pointed* white beard. About the same weight as the Green Monkey, the Diana is much longer and more slender.

Of all the *Cercopithecus* monkeys, the Diana is the most completely arboreal, corresponding in this respect to the Red Colobus among the Colobus group. It is restricted to mature forests, where it lives a frugivorous life in the upper branches. The troops, of up to thirty strong, feed over a wide area. The members of a troop may be spread over a quarter of a mile of forest—a very long way compared to the troops of other species. They keep in touch by means of their trilling utterances, some of which are difficult to distinguish from the calls of the Green Parrot. The male's full call is rather complicated: 'ki-ki-ki-ki-*kyow* ki-ki-*kyow*'. There is a variety of other calls; indeed, the Diana vies with the Mona in vocal virtuosity.

The Diana also vies with the Mona as a pet. Lively, affectionate and very decorative, it suffers only from being rather harder to keep. Care must be taken to provide sufficient variety in diet. It does not seem to do so well when caged in company with other monkeys, and greatly appreciates individual attention. The males may become dangerous when about four or five years old.

The Diana is becoming rare, and should be protected.

21. The Spot-nosed Monkey

Cercopithecus petaurista

(*Plate VI, 21*)

There are several kinds of monkey with white nose-spots. They have been quite wrongly lumped together as 'Putty-nosed Monkeys', not only by ordinary people, but even by scientists, who should have known better. In the Spot-nosed Monkeys, the nose-spot is very neat and heart-shaped, the hair of the forehead and crown is short, and the throat and underparts are pure white. They are about the same size as the Monas. There are two races, found in the forest from Togoland westward. As usual, the Ghanaian race differs in small ways from that found in Sierra Leone.

Where it occurs, the Spot-nosed Monkey is perhaps the commonest of all. Living on both fruit and leaves, it frequents the lower layers of the forest, and is especially common in thickets. Hence it is particularly well suited to secondary forest, coastal scrub and the fringing forests in Guinea Savannah. Because of its catholic taste in food, a troop can support itself in quite a small patch of forest, such as would be insufficient to feed a troop of Monas or Colobus of equal size.

This is a fairly silent monkey in the wild state. Though it has a fair vocabulary, the bark of the male is the cry most frequently heard. It is a deep and resonant 'ke-urr'.

In Western Nigeria there is a closely related species, *Cercopithecus erythrogaster*, in which the nose-spot may be red, yellow or white, and the belly red or grey. It does not seem to be so successful as the western species, though it is similar in its habits.

22. The Putty-nosed Monkey

Cercopithecus nictitans

(*Plate VI, 22*)

These rather larger white-nosed monkeys occur in Nigeria and in the western Ivory Coast and Liberia. The distinction between the three geographic races is not important, but it is as well to be able to distinguish the Putty-nosed from the

Spot-nosed groups. First, in build and in general attitude, the Putty-nose resembles the Monas, perhaps partly on account of its longish fur, which makes it look more sturdy. In detail, the nose-spot is a large, rather irregularly diamond-shaped mark, not so pure white as in the Spot-nose. The fur of the crown and forehead is longer, making the head appear bigger. The fur of the underparts is rather a dirty white. Finally, the whole animal appears very much darker in colour.

The Putty-nose, like the Spot-nose, eats leaves as well as fruits. The teeth, as in all leaf-eating monkeys, are covered with black 'tartar'.

The diet introduces an interesting point. In Nigeria, the Putty-nose is a very successful creature, while the representative of the Spot-nose group, as we saw on the last page, is much more rare. In Liberia and the western Ivory Coast, the reverse is the case: the Spot-nose is found everywhere, the Putty-nose is restricted to the mature High Forest. Evidently these two groups of monkeys are in such close competition for food and other necessities of life, that in one part of West Africa one group has come out on top, while the position is reversed in the other region.

In captivity, both groups are easy to keep, but they are quieter and less attractive than Monas, though undoubtedly superior to the Green Monkeys as pets.

23. The Red Patas Monkey   (*Plate VI, 23*)

Erythrocebus patas

With its very long legs, this is a real greyhound among monkeys. The rusty red colour is very handsome, but the part black, part white face gives particularly the youngsters a comic appearance. It is, except for the Baboon, the tallest of West African monkeys, but by no means the heaviest. A big male will only weigh eighteen pounds or so.

Of all the monkeys, the Red Patas is the least likely to be seen in forest or thick cover of any kind. Indeed, it only ventures into such places when they contain the local water supply. It is much more at home among the grass and scattered trees of the savannah.

Very little is known of its diet, since those which are seen or shot while feeding are mostly surprised during a crop-raid. It seems, however, that it is mainly a fruit eater. In captivity, roots are taken also, and this may be true in the bush. It has been claimed, with, in my experience, some justification, that the Red Patas is the hardest savannah mammal in Africa to stalk and kill. As with the baboons, there is always one member of the troop so placed that he can see the country around. Even as they travel from one feeding-ground to another, they play a kind of leap-frog. A leading monkey will ascend a tree to survey the landscape while the rest of the troop pass below. Then he will descend and run along with the others, while another takes his turn. Their galloping is apparently lazy, but exceedingly rapid. The young are sometimes left behind to conceal themselves behind tufts of grass when danger threatens.

The voice is normally harsh, but they are capable of uttering an eerie moaning sound, which can be very wearing if you have one about the house.

24. The Mangabey Monkey   (*Plate VII, 24*)

Cercocebus torquatus

The Mangabeys' are also called White-eyelid Monkeys. The name is self-explanatory, and the white eyelids are much in evidence in captivity, for Mangabeys are greatly addicted to grimacing. They are quite large creatures, about the weight of a Red Patas, though not quite so tall. The fur is basically a smoky grey colour, variously ornamented—not at all in the Sierra Leone race, white-crowned in the Ghana race, and with a white collar and chestnut head-markings in the eastern species (*C. torquatus*).

They are found throughout the High Forest zone, except, apparently, in western Nigeria. They prefer swampy areas.

Palm-swamps and rice farms are important sources of food, and they can be a great pest to the farmer. They are, in fact, the typical fruit-eating monkeys of the lowest layers of the High Forest, and spend a great deal of their time on the ground. In consequence, they are sometimes very difficult to hunt, though rather easier to trap than most forest monkeys.

Most of the calls they utter are staccato in nature, a many-syllabled chuckle or chattering sound.

In many features of their anatomy and behaviour they resemble the Baboon. The smacking of the lips, the naughtiness (and frequent punishment) of the young, the quarrelling over food and the daytime love-life are all very baboon-like characteristics.

I have always had a suspicion that the Mangabey is the most intelligent of all West African monkeys, with the possible exception of the Baboon. They are certainly the most sympathetic towards a human being. Unfortunately, they suffer from an irrepressible tendency to mischief, and from being rather large, and not particularly decorative.

25. The Olive Baboon   (*Plate VII, 25*)

Papio anubis choras

This huge, speckled olive-brown monkey is an inhabitant of the savannah zones, and is found throughout West Africa except some parts of the extreme west, where it is locally replaced by the rather different, reddish Western Baboon, *P. papio.* The male is truly a formidable beast, and many (largely unsubstantiated) tales are told of his wanton savagery. A large male weighs up to five stone, but it is possible that even heavier specimens exist. The females, on the other hand, attain only half that weight, and, in captivity at any rate, are much more docile and gentle in disposition.

Baboons feed on roots, fruits and shoots, not disdaining a little animal food, including scorpions and lizards if they are chanced upon. They can tackle even such large and hard fruits as the Baobab, crunching them up with their massive jaws quite easily.

A troop generally consists of at least twenty monkeys, sometimes many more, led by the strongest male. He is usually to be seen in a prominent position on a rock or a tree. He will even act 'policeman' on occasion while the rest of the troop crosses a road. Leopard and Man are the chief enemies of Baboons. It is interesting to observe that the big canine teeth of a male Baboon are considerably longer and sharper than those of a Leopard, but it is all too rarely that the Baboon gets the chance to use them. Nevertheless, woe betide the foolish dog who thinks he can treat a Baboon with contempt. He will end his life terribly mangled, and, for good measure, disembowelled.

Baboons are not recommended as pets.

26. The Chimpanzee

(*Plate VII, 26*)

Pan troglodytes

The Chimpanzee belongs to the Ape group. Apes are very closely related indeed to Man. They are tailless. Monkeys use their tails as balancers when walking or leaping about the trees. Apes, lacking tails, climb with all four feet, but when making a traverse along a branch, or when passing from one branch to another, they generally swing by their arms, the branch above, the Ape beneath. That way, they do not need a balancer. On the ground, they walk on all fours, using the side of the foot and the knuckles, not the palm of the hand. The arms are very long and strong, the legs rather short. The hands are very man-like, but the foot has the 'opposable' first toe as in monkeys. Apes in general and Chimps in particular possess very great manipulative skill, and a large brain, which is very similar to that of Man, though still considerably smaller.

BABOON. *Mende:* kongongola. *Twi:* kontromfi. *Ewe:* kese. *Dagbane:* kparle. *Igbo:* adaka. *Yoruba:* ọbọ. *Hausa:* bika.

30

Chimps live in small family parties in West Africa, though larger troops are sometimes reported. They are in most places very rare, confined to mature High Forest. This is largely because of the activities of hunters. Where guns are few or the animal is sacred, they may become a pest in the farmland. They live mainly on fruits.

Many stories are told of Chimp 'drumming and dancing' meetings in the depths of the forest. It is certainly true that the creatures will beat on a hollow tree-trunk, revelling in the sound it makes. Like men, also, they delight in the hideous noises they can utter, which at close quarters can be quite frightening to the lonely hunter.

Chimps probably never reproduce before they are ten years old, and, like monkeys, normally have only one offspring. Hence the ease with which they can be, and are being, exterminated for the sake of a little meat or a little prestige.

27. The Gorilla   (*Plate VII, 27*)

Gorilla gorilla

While the Chimp is considerably inferior in stature to Man (though the males are very heavy), the male Gorilla may easily reach Man's height, and is two or three times Man's weight. The Gorilla is found within our area only in the Cameroons, and even there it is very rare. It is very like a large Chimp in appearance, and as in that animal, its enormous strength is largely in the arms and chest. The legs are short, and though it spends a good deal of time on the ground, it is unable to walk upright more than a few steps.

Notwithstanding its great bulk and strength, and its formidable teeth, it is a harmless vegetarian. At least, it may harm crops occasionally, and if attacked it may even harm Man, but on the whole its reputation for ferocity is unjustified.

CHIMPANZEE. *Mende:* ngolo. *Twi:* akaatia. *Ewe:* akplakpoe. *Igbo:* ɔzɔ di mgba. *Yoruba:* inake.

Family parties of Gorilla are said to be quite small, only up to ten or so strong. Like Chimpanzees, Gorillas are said to build nests in the branches, in which the females and young rest at night. These nests consist of stout branches and twigs torn from young trees. The male generally has a nest on the ground. This doubtless gives some degree of protection from marauding Leopards, which might otherwise attack females and young. The nests are most insanitary.

Unfortunately, we still know very little about the habits of wild gorillas, for fact is too much mixed up with inaccuracy and downright fiction. And it is all too likely that before we have a chance to find out, there will be no Gorillas left in West Africa. The fauna of High Forest is admittedly more difficult to protect than that of savannah, but the case for protection of the Apes is clear; if Governments are afraid of producing legislation, at least a few influential private citizens could do a great deal in districts where Chimps and Gorillas still exist.

Plate VII

25

27

24

26

Scale

0   1   2   3 ft.

24 Mangabey Monkey   26 Chimpanzee

25 Olive Baboon   27 Gorilla

Plate VIII

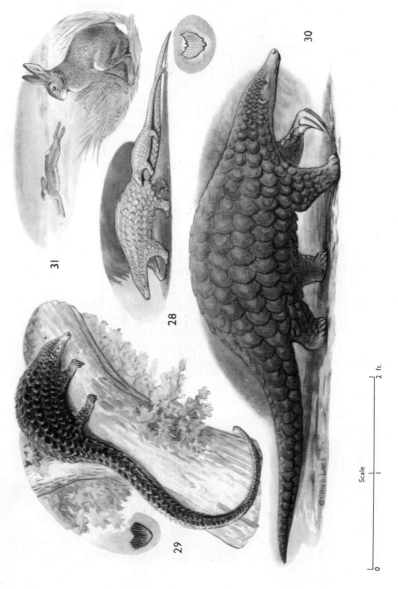

28 White-bellied Pangolin   30 Giant Ground Pangolin

29 Black-bellied Pangolin   31 Togo Hare

Plate IX

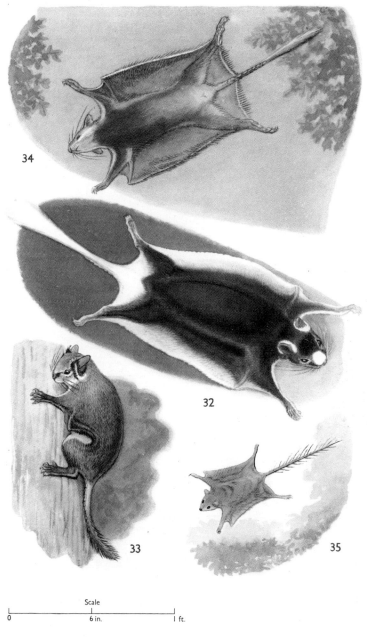

32 Pel's Flying Squirrel   34 Beecroft's Flying Squirrel

33 Derby's Flying Squirrel   35 Pygmy Flying Squirrel

Plate X

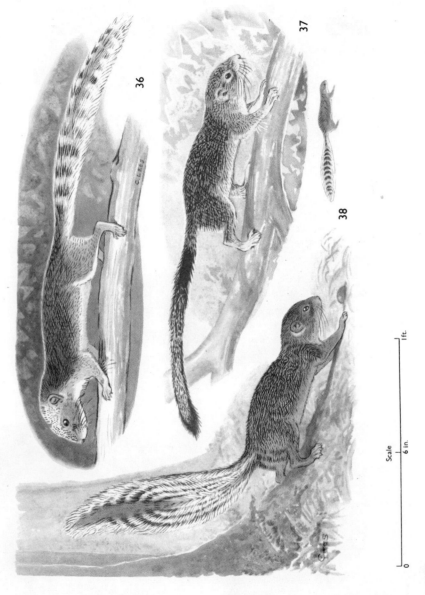

36 Giant Forest Squirrel 38 Red-headed Forest Squirrel
37 Slender-tailed Squirrel

PHOLIDOTA

The austere name at the head of the page distinguishes the Pangolins, or Scaly Ant-eaters. There are three species in West Africa. All are much alike in general appearance, and all live exclusively on ants or termites. The upper surface of the body, the sides and the outer limbs, as well as the whole of the tail, are covered in scales. These scales are large and horny, over-lapping like the scales of many fishes and snakes. Only the front of the head, the underparts and the inner parts of the limbs are covered in normal mammalian hair.

Pangolins can roll themselves into a ball like the Hedgehog, and then they present a difficult problem to the would-be attacker, for all the hair-covered surface is then invisible, and only the scales show. They have tiny ears, rather small eyes, and no teeth. The very long tongue, covered in sticky saliva, is used for collecting the ants or termites. In fact, it is a bait, which the ants automatically attack when it is thrust into their nests. The Pangolin breaks the nest open by means of its powerful front claws, one of which is enormously enlarged as a digging tool.

28. The White-bellied Pangolin   (*Plate VIII, 28*)

Manis tricuspis

Also called the Three-cusped Pangolin, this species is over a foot long, with a tail of over two feet. The scales are a plain dirty brown, the belly a (usually) dirty white. It lives

---

PANGOLIN. *Mende:* kainya.   *Twi:* aprawa.   *Ewe:* luɣuluɣui.   *Igbo:* aka abɔ.   *Yoruba:* āka.
Particular species—*M.:* kimba (*giant ground*).   *T.:* aprawabene (*black-bellied*), opra (*giant ground*).   *E.:* hotoklolo (*giant ground*), kpla, atopra, lumo.

in trees in the High Forest zone, using the tail as an aid to climbing and as a powerful prehensile anchor. It is nocturnal and solitary. A single offspring is produced, which while very young clings on the mother's back at the root of the tail.

29. The Black-bellied Pangolin (*Plate VIII, 29*)
Manis tetradactyla

The second Tree Pangolin is a little larger than the first. The scales here are black, bordered with bright red-brown and off-white at the tip. All the haired portions of the body are jet black. Unlike its relatives, it feeds in the daytime. It seems particularly fond of the large red tree ants. Though it also is a High Forest form, it does not seem to be quite so widespread in drier forests as the White-bellied Pangolin.

30. The Giant Ground Pangolin (*Plate VIII, 30*)
Manis gigantea

This is a real monster of a Pangolin, up to three feet long, with a three-foot tail. Too heavy for the trees, it lives on the ground, feeding largely on termites. The enormous tail has here lost some of its value as a prehensile organ, but is useful as an extra prop when the animal sits on its hind legs to break open a hard termite mound with its powerful front claws. It is nocturnal, and lives in both the forested and the savannah regions of West Africa.

Probably the only animals powerful enough to kill this creature are Lion, Leopard and Man. Even so, late in 1955, in Sefwi in Ghana, a hunter heard a tremendous commotion in the bush, and found a Giant Pangolin, somewhat scarred, dragging through the forest with its tail the recently-dead body of a Leopard. The Pangolin's tail was round the Leopard's neck, and had obviously been the means of turning the tables on the attacked. The hunter finished the Pangolin with a blow of his cutlass on the back of the unprotected head.

HARES AND RODENTS

The Rabbits and Hares on the one hand and the Rodents on the other are two entirely separate groups which have a great deal in common. Though there are in fact many differences, I shall only mention one. In the Rodents there are only two upper and two lower front teeth; in Rabbits and Hares, the two upper teeth are supplemented by another very tiny pair but behind the big ones. The front teeth are very important in both groups. Between them and the cheek-teeth there is a gap, so that the functions of the two sets are kept separate. The front teeth are used in gnawing, or biting off the food. They are as sharp as chisels, and are always growing, so that they never become worn out. The back teeth are flat and rough, and are used for grinding the food up. A good chewing is particularly important, for most of these animals eat rather coarse vegetable matter, which would otherwise be indigestible. The gap between the two sets of teeth is used in this way: many of the fruits eaten by Rodents have a very hard, quite inedible shell. A hole can be made by the front teeth, and the lips brought round behind to prevent even the smallest particle from reaching the back teeth, which it would damage, or, even more important, the gut. It is interesting to note that many Rodents are quite capable of gnawing through lead, zinc and other soft metals. Some are accused of eating ivory!

Mainly small creatures, they make up for their lack of size in their variety and abundance, the latter partly achieved by the rapidity with which they reproduce. Many of them avoid their enemies by moving at night, living in burrows and so on, but they are all important in the diet of flesh-eating mammals, birds and reptiles. Many of them are also serious agricultural and domestic pests.

35

31. The Togo Hare (*Plate VIII, 31*)

Lepus capensis zechi

The Togo Hare is the common Hare of the Guinea Savannah. (The Sudan Savannah has another species.) It is grey-brown, speckled with black, with a light-coloured belly and a few pure white hairs on the forehead.

There are no wild Rabbits in West Africa. The differences between Rabbits and Hares are small but important. Rabbits live and reproduce in burrows, coming out only at feeding-time. The young are born naked, blind and defenceless in a nest made of fur and leaves. Litters are large, seven or eight being quite a normal number of young. Hares never burrow. The Togo Hare normally has only two young at a birth, and they are born with a normal covering of fur, with their eyes open, in a rough nest in the grass. All Hares behave in this manner.

The Togo Hare is nocturnal and solitary. Its food is grass, but the grass must be tender. Such food is not always plentiful in the savannah, and the Hare must therefore range far in a single night. Hence it is a far rarer animal than the Cutting Grass.

Some northern tribes consider it bad luck to kill a Hare. Again, some Europeans believe it to be a foul feeder, and will not eat it. So on the whole it is not persecuted by Man to the extent which its excellent meat would seem to justify.

This is doubtless the species which has achieved world-wide fame as 'Brer Rabbit' of the American Negro folk-tales. It certainly figures in many of the West African legends from which the Uncle Remus stories were derived.

HARE. *Twi:* adanko. *Ewe:* fɔmizi. *Dagbane:* sooŋa. *Igbo:* ulili. *Yoruba:* ehoro. *Hausa:* zōmo.

SCALY-TAILED FLYING SQUIRRELS

I am going to call these creatures Flying Squirrels for short. They are not actually Squirrels, and they don't actually fly: they only glide. But it is both a convenient and an expressive name. There are three large and two pygmy species in West Africa. I shall deal with the large ones first.

These animals are about the size of large squirrels, are of slender build and have long tails. Unlike that of Squirrels, the fur is as beautifully soft as a Persian cat's, their ears are naked and projecting, they have scales under the tail, and there is a gliding membrane.

The gliding membrane takes the form of flaps of skin, densely furred above and more sparsely below, which stretch on either side from wrist to ankle and from ankle to tail base. The Flying Squirrels can launch themselves into the air, spread out their legs (and with them the gliding membrane) and plane from one tree to another. If the animal starts from a high enough branch, over a hundred yards may be covered in this way. There is, of course, appreciable loss of height, but the whole effect is most graceful and effortless.

When landing, the Flying Squirrels generally choose a vertical tree trunk. Just before they land, they stall, head up, tail down. They then make a landing with all four feet together. Actually it is a five-point landing, for this is where the scaly tail comes in. The scales are so placed as to grip the bark of the tree and prevent the animal from slipping backward. They

---

SQUIRREL. *Mende:* (see below). *Twi:* akye. *Ewe:* kasanui. *Dagbane:* tibeya. *Igbo:* ɔsa. *Yoruba:* okere. *Hausa:* ɓeran.
Particular species—*M.:* bɔvi (*red legged*), sese (*small green*), kaikulo (*ground*), kponde, nguahi. *Twi.:* ɔha (*Pel's flying*), ɔhatwiritwiriw (*pygmy flying*), kukuban (*giant forest*), opurosrɛbere (*slender-tailed*), kontodoɔ (*red headed*), ɔsereben (*red-legged*), apetebi (*side-striped*), amɔakua (*ground*), purohema, akyerekye. *E.:* kasanui. *D.:* sinsirega (*ground*), larenga (*Gambian*). *I.:* oghu (*flying*), uzɛ (*giant forest*). *Y.:* ikun (*ground*). *H.:* kusun bisa, kwaga, makwarna, mādaidaici, wutamfa, dangwal.

37

are also useful when the animal is climbing a vertical trunk; this it does in a curious manner, gripping with the fore-claws and humping its back to drag the hind-quarters and tail up, then gripping with the hind claws and scaly tail while it extends the body to take a fresh grip with the fore-claws.

All the larger species eat leaves, flowers, and occasionally fruits and are impossible to keep in captivity.

32. Pel's Flying Squirrel (Plate IX, 32)
Anomalurus peli

Over two and a half feet long (half of it tail), this species is entirely black and white. The colour scheme is (broadly) black above and white below, with a white tail, though all black individuals and reddish ones have been found occasionally. It is found only in the taller trees of the High Forest zone from the Volta to Liberia. Where it occurs, it is the commonest Flying Squirrel by far.

This species is nocturnal, spending the day in hollow trees which have a high exit-hole. It feeds mainly on leaves, but also takes flowers. Its call is a low 'puru-puru'.

33. Derby's Flying Squirrel (Plate IX, 33)
Anomalurus durbianus

This rather smaller, green-grey species has habits similar to the last, but does not frequent hollow trees. It lies up in dense foliage, curled up almost into a ball. It occurs all over the High Forest zone, and is the typical nocturnal Flying Squirrel of most parts of the African dense forest.

34. Beecroft's Flying Squirrel (*Plate IX, 34*)

Anomalurops beecrofti

About the size of Derby's, or a little smaller, this species has a beautiful orange throat and chest. Unlike the other two species, it is diurnal. It seems to be commonest in the drier forests, though it actually occurs all over the West African High Forest zone.

All the Flying Squirrels have but a single young at a time, so far as we know. Until it is independent, the baby is said to cling to the mother's back.

35. The Pygmy Flying Squirrels (*Plate IX, 35*)

Idiurus spp.

These are tiny versions, weighing about one ounce, of the Scaly-tailed Flying Squirrels. They are about four inches long, with a five-inch tail. The fur, as in the large species, is soft, but a dull brown colour. The tail though scaly below as normal, also has long hairs arranged in rows along the edges, in a fashion which is unique. This arrangement is difficult to explain, but is doubtless concerned with the mechanics of gliding.

Though there are two species in West Africa, I am familiar with only one, Cansdale's Pygmy Flying Squirrel, *I. kivuensis cansdalei*. This is apparently fairly common in the High Forest zone of Ghana. Related forms occur in the Cameroons, and doubtless in other parts of West Africa.

The animal, unlike any of the larger species, lives in colonies. Tall hollow trees are its normal home, but it may also be found on dead trees with flaking bark. In the latter case, it crawls under a bark-flake to rest during the day. I have found up to a dozen living together. Sanderson found flocks of 'hundreds' in the Cameroons. When driven out in the daytime, their gliding is rather erratic in my experience (though again Sanderson differs). There seems to be a good deal of weaving

39

to and fro, possibly because insufficient initial speed is gained from the first leap from the tree.

A colony may live, apparently peaceably, in company with colonies of the Grizzled Leaf-nosed Bat, with Pel's Flying Squirrel or with Dormice.

The food of these creatures has not been fully investigated. I have only found fruits in the stomach, but they are suspected also of taking insects.

GIANT SQUIRRELS

36. The Giant Forest Squirrel *(Plate X, 36)*

Protoxerus strangeri

This enormous Squirrel is rather an ungainly creature. About eleven inches long, with a thirteen-inch tail, it often weighs over two pounds. What is immediately striking, however, is the size and weight of the head, which appears quite disproportionately large. The speckled fur is a warm brown colour on the upper surface, with a silvery-grey head. The under-fur is very sparse and white, the pale yellow colour of the skin showing through. The ears are small, covered in short fur, and carried close to the side of the head as in all the West African Squirrels. In this species, the fur is very harsh in texture, though not so much so as in the Ground Squirrel.

Like all the Squirrels, it is diurnal, and like most of them it spends almost all its life in trees. It is a High Forest species, occurring wherever sufficient tall timber remains to allow it to find nesting-holes far from the ground. It does, however, inhabit fringing forests along the rivers well into the Guinea Savannah, despite the fact that the trees there are a good deal lower than it would normally inhabit in the High Forest proper.

It seems to feed in any layer of the forest, even coming down to the ground occasionally. Its food is entirely fruits. The great head and jaws enable it to tackle very hard foods which are too much for smaller species. It is very fond of ripe Raphia.

Rather clumsy in its movements, it normally runs along the

Plate XI

39

40

41

42

Scale

0 1 2 3 4 5 6 ins.

Clifford Lees

39 Gambian Sun Squirrel   41 Red-legged Sun Squirrel

40 Small Forest Squirrel   42 Small Green Squirrel

Plate XII

43   Orange-headed Squirrel   45   Green Side-striped Squirrel

44   Red Side-striped Squirrel   46   West African Ground Squirrel

Plate XIII

Scale

0   1   2   3   4 ins.

47   Large Grey Dormouse   49   Slender Gerbil

48   Small Dormouse   50   Kemp's Gerbil

Plate XIV

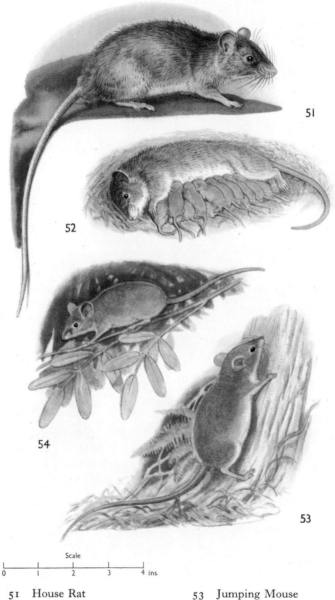

51

52

54

53

Scale

0 1 2 3 4 ins.

51 House Rat   53 Jumping Mouse

52 Multimammate Rat   54 Climbing Wood Mouse

larger branches. When it does move through the foliage, it makes more noise than many a Monkey.

The cry is a resonant chuckle. I do not believe that it 'booms'. That noise is made by the Mona Monkey.

37. The Slender-tailed Squirrel (*Plate X, 37*)

Protoxerus aubinnii

This large High Forest species is almost entirely uniform dark olive in colour. It is nine or ten inches long, with a rather slender twelve-inch tail, in which the spread of the hairs is mainly outwards, not an all-round bushy effect such as is found in most other Squirrels.

It is found only from the Volta westward, and is almost never seen in secondary or farmed forest. Nevertheless, in really mature forest in the moister areas, it is quite as common as the Giant Forest Squirrel: indeed, it would seem to some extent that it replaces that species in the moister forests. Like most Squirrels, it is entirely frugivorous. Nothing is known of its nests and young, and little of its whole way of life.

38. The Red-headed Forest Squirrel (*Plate X, 38*)

Epixerus ebii

Though it is known only from Sierra Leone, Ghana and the Cameroons, and is everywhere accounted rare, this very handsome species probably occurs all over the High Forest zone except for Western Nigeria. It has not only the red head which gives it its name, but also a red underside and inner limbs. The tail is magnificent, with black and white hairs and a red understreak. I have only seen it in moist High Forest, near rivers and streams where Raphia is plentiful. It frequently comes to the ground. On the other hand, in Sierra Leone it is so far only known from a mountain area.

The two Squirrels described on this page show how very little we know of the small mammals which do not normally tolerate cultivated areas.

SUN SQUIRRELS
Heliosciurus spp.

This is a large, well-known group of many species and races. All are practically uniform in colour on the upper surface, the hairs being almost black, but tipped or ringed with white, yellow or reddish tints. The whole effect is speckled grey, green or brown according to the species, race, or even season of the year. There are four main subdivisions, which may well be called species.

39. The Gambian Sun Squirrel *(Plate XI, 39)*
Heliosciurus gambianus

This is the only tree-squirrel found in typical Guinea Savannah. It is greyish above, white below, and the tail has pronounced rings of dark and light fur. It grows to about eight inches with a ten-inch tail. It nests in the hollows frequently to be found in gnarled old savannah trees, and favours areas where it can jump from tree to tree without coming down to the ground too often. Its food is mainly rather dry fruits, and it is said to lay up a store of these during seasons of plenty, and to use part of the store during the dry season.

40. The Small Forest Squirrel *(Plate XI, 40)*
Heliosciurus punctatus

Smaller and darker in colour than the Gambian, this Sun-squirrel is about six inches long with an eight-inch tail. The underparts are lighter than the back, but never white.

The Small Forest Squirrel is a High Forest species, found from the Volta westward. It lives in both mature and secondary forest, and often invades farms, including cocoa and oil-palm plantations. It is something of a pest. The nest is made in a tree hole, at some distance from the ground.

41. The Red-legged Sun Squirrel (*Plate XI, 41*)

Heliosciurus rufobrachium

This is a High Forest species, very variable in colour. The main distinguishing character apart from the size is that there is always either a deep red, buff or orange tinge to the underparts, especially round the groin and armpits. The tail is never so markedly ringed as in the Gambian Squirrel. This species is about nine or ten inches long, with an eleven-inch tail.

It nests rather high up, but the sites chosen are as usual for the group. It feeds in any layer of the forest, and readily takes to a life in farmland and secondary bush. Like the Small Forest Squirrel, it may become a pest. It will take insects as well as fruits in captivity, but then the same is true of monkeys, which are normally entirely vegetarian in the bush.

42. The Small Green Squirrel (*Plate XI, 42*)

Heliosciurus poensis

Unlike the other Sun Squirrels, this species has a very soft coat and a rather slender tail. It is minutely speckled black and green, with lighter underparts. It is only six inches long at most, with a seven-inch tail.

The Small Green Squirrel lives from the Volta westward and from the Cross eastward in the High Forest zone. It frequents areas where undergrowth is dense, and is especially common in neglected farms and secondary bush. Like the Side-striped Squirrels, it nests in dense foliage.

SIDE-STRIPED SQUIRRELS

Funisciurus spp.

These Squirrels all have very soft fur like the Small Green Squirrel, and all have a stripe, white or yellowish, down the flank. In addition, they all carry the tail arched in an S-shape over the back like a European Squirrel. The tail is always shorter than the head and body.

43. The Orange-headed Squirrel (*Plate XII, 43*)

Funisciurus auriculatus

A High Forest form found only from the Volta eastward, this is a really beautiful species It is much rarer than the common forms described below, and much larger, about nine inches long with an eight-inch tail. I have only found it in mature High Forest. It may be recognised by the orange head, and by the side stripe, which is actually a series of distinct spots in a row.

44. The Red Side-striped Squirrel (*Plate XII, 44*)

Funisciurus pyrrhopus

45. The Green Side-striped Squirrel (*Plate XII, 45*)

Funisciurus substriatus

In various forms, representatives of one or both of these groups are found all over the High Forest zone, and occasionally in Guinea Savannah. Some are mainly red and black on the upper surface, others mainly green. They are about seven and a half inches long with a six and a half-inch tail. All are skulkers in undergrowth, more often heard than seen. The calls of Squirrels are confusing, but one call of the smaller Side-striped Squirrels is unmistakable. It is a strident, bird-like 'clack-clack-clack-clack', going down the scale. These Squirrels live and nest in thick undergrowth, and are very common and harmful to cocoa and other crops.

44

GROUND SQUIRRELS

46. The West African Ground Squirrel *(Plate XII, 46)*

Xerus erythropus

This is a large Squirrel, as big in body as the Giant Forest Squirrel, but with a shorter tail. I shall not describe it in detail, save to point out that it is mainly sandy in colour, with very coarse fur and a white side stripe, and it is the only Ground Squirrel in our area.

Diurnal like its tree-dwelling relatives, it is a burrower, and hides and bears its young below ground. The burrows when not also breeding places are often quite simple, a straight tunnel with two exit-holes. On the other hand the more permanent headquarters used for breeding are often veritable warrens. One or two of the exit-holes are usually temporarily blocked, and provide emergency escape routes when unwelcome visitors such as cobras drop in, or when humans try to dig the animals out.

The main food of the Ground Squirrel is roots, though fallen fruit is also taken, and occasionally the animal will climb trees to get fruits before they fall. It is a great pest on farms, and destroys quantities of yam and cassava. Its invasion of the High Forest zone has been markedly successful, indeed a forest subspecies has evolved. As yet, however, it has not penetrated the more remote unexploited areas.

The Ground Squirrel is a common sight on the roads and footpaths, which it uses with impunity in its travels in search of food. It is difficult to shoot, and a desirable reduction in its numbers could only be attained by systematic trapping, or by allowing snakes, hawks and mongooses to breed in peace.

DORMICE

Graphiurus spp.

There are probably only two species of Dormouse in West Africa, a larger and a smaller, though the latter is known under many different names. The soft fur, bushy tail and naked, forward-pointing ears (like those of a Flying Squirrel) serve to distinguish them from all other Rodents.

47. The Large Grey Dormouse (*Plate XIII*, *47*)
Graphiurus hueti

This species is uniformly greyish or reddish in colour, the young being a beautiful dove-grey. Fully grown it is about five and a half inches long, with a four-inch tail. It lives only in the High Forest zone, in colonies of up to a dozen, which occupy tall hollow trees. They are often to be found in company with other mammals. It is nocturnal, feeding both on fruits and on insects. The meat is regarded as a delicacy, and hollow trees are regularly smoked to obtain it.

48. The Small Dormouse (*Plate XIII*, *48*)
Graphiurus spurrelli

This is a much smaller animal, only about three and a half to four inches long. Its colour is like that of the larger species. It occurs both in forest and savannah. Although common enough, it is mostly seen round houses, and we know very little of its life in the bush, save that it is nocturnal and lives in trees. In houses, it seems to eat insects for the most part. It can often be seen hunting on the outside of mosquito-netting. It is an infernal pest to anyone who keeps an aviary, for it will kill and eat captive birds.

The Gerbils are Rodents of the Rat group, but are in some ways rather odd. Most of them have unusually long hind legs and feet, and a long, smooth-haired tail with a little tuft at the tip. These characteristics are connected with the way the animal moves. Most Gerbils, when they are in a hurry, hop along on their hind feet. The power from the hop comes from the long back legs, and the long tail acts as a balancer, preventing the animal from falling forward on to its front legs. All Gerbils are normally savannah dwellers. Some (though not the ones described here) are able to live in very dry semi-desert regions.

49. The Slender Gerbil *(Plate XIII, 49)*

Taterillus gracilis

This is the smallest of the Guinea Savannah Gerbils. About five inches long, it has a tail of eight inches, with a little tuft of long hairs at the tip. It is a handsome little creature, with a warm brown back, bright buff flanks and a pure white throat, chest and belly. It lives in small colonies in burrows, coming out to feed at night. One may see it hopping across the road in the headlights of a car. It often lives in cultivated areas, where it may do some damage.

The Guinea Gerbil, *Tatera guineae*

This Gerbil is of the same proportions and almost the same colour as the last, but is larger—nearly as big as Kemp's Gerbil. It also lives in Guinea Savannah, and can make its burrows in the hardest ground. It is not found in colonies, so far as we know.

50. Kemp's Gerbil (*Plate XIII, 50*)

Tateri kempi

This is the largest and heaviest, and at the same time the least typical of the Gerbils. It is about seven inches long, with a tail of the same length, and untufted at the tip. The hind feet, though long compared to most Rats of similar size, are actually only about the same length as those of the Slender Gerbil. The colour pattern is the same as in the other species, but darker and duller as a whole.

Kemp's Gerbil rarely if ever hops. Certainly I have never seen it do so. It is nocturnal like the others, and lives in burrows, generally two animals to a burrow. Its food is roots of various kinds, the thick roots of savannah grasses or yam, cassava and other crops. Although it was without doubt originally a savannah form, it has invaded the High Forest zone in areas which have long been cultivated, and where grasses have encroached into the forest. The root crops grown there, which are mostly not native to Africa, such as cocoyam, cassava and sweet potato, form an ideal food supply and Kemp's Gerbil is a very considerable pest.

Owls, snakes and small predatory mammals are probably its main enemies. In a long-cultivated region like the Accra Plain, this virtually means that it has, thanks to Man's short-sightedness, no enemies at all. The owls lack nesting-places (the trees have been cut down), the snakes are ruthlessly killed, and the small predatory mammals have been hunted out for the sake of a little meat. In consequence, Kemp's Gerbil flourishes, and the cassava is terribly ravaged.

This common pest is only a single example of what Man can do to his own detriment when he thoughtlessly upsets the 'balance of nature'.

Plate XV

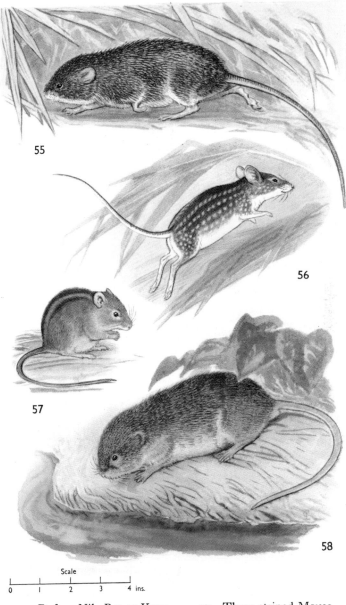

55

56

57

58

Scale

0   1   2   3   4 ins.

55 Rufous Nile Rat or Kusu   57 Three-striped Mouse
56 Spotted Grass Mouse   58 Shaggy Rat

Plate XVI

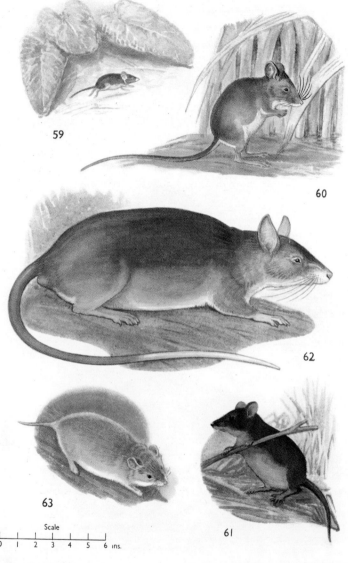

59 Pygmy Mouse

60 Swamp Rat

61 Rufous-bellied Rat

62 Pouched Rat or Giant Rat

63 Fat Mouse

RATS AND MICE

51. The House Rat

(*Plate XIV, 51*)

Rattus rattus

The House Rat, which originally came from India, is now established in most parts of the world. West Africa is no exception. In most towns and many villages, in forest and savannah regions alike, it is to be found in abundance, using Man's houses for shelter, Man's food for sustenance, and Man's goods of all kinds for nesting materials. In appearance it is the typical Rat. It is about seven inches long, with a naked tail measuring a further nine inches. There are three common colour phases. The commonest is the Black Rat, *R. r. rattus*. This is very dark blue-grey, almost black on the back. Next comes the Alexandrine Rat, *R.r. alexandrinus*. This is grey-brown, again darkest on the back, but with a very light grey belly. Finally there is the Cream-bellied Rat, *R.r. frugivorus*, which is much like the Alexandrine Rat, but lighter, and with a pure white or cream belly.

You will find books often refer to the three races as if they were different animals. In fact, they can interbreed, and are no more different than red fowls, white fowls and speckled fowls. They are all House Rats, and they should all be slaughtered on sight.

The House Rat is a good climber, and frequently makes roofs and garden trees its headquarters. Though vegetable food is probably preferred, a hungry House Rat will eat

---

RAT. *Mende:* tondo. *Twi:* akura. *Ewe:* (e)di. *Dagbane:* gyeŋbarega. *Igbo:* okɛ ɛnɔ. *Yoruba:* ekute. *Hausa:* ɓera.
Particular species—*M.:* ndonde nyina (*Nile*), folo-gbete (*spotted mouse*), lende (*striped mouse*), mbɔ nyina (*rufous bellied*), kiwulo (*giant*), rɔlo, lele. *T.:* abotokura (*spotted mouse*), akurasono (*striped mouse*), akurakuma (*pygmy*), okisi (*pouched*). *E.:* gbaxlẽ (*spotted mouse*), gbefi (*striped mouse*), akpagana (*pygmy*), alegeli (*giant*), aminoe, badafi, atitomefi, adzɔkofi, zatɔe. *D.:* dayuyo (*giant*), sɔbele. *I.:* mbɛ (*pygmy*), ɛyi (*pouched*). *Y.:* ago (*striped*), ɛliri (*pygmy*), okete (*pouched*). *H.:* kūsu, ɗamɓarya, ƙiye, nadōgōro, ɓagi, tsiyo (*field*).

anything from lizards and cockroaches to candles and soap. The only effective way of keeping down House Rats in your own premises is to keep a cat. Traps and poison work only for a short time, for House Rats are very cunning, and there is always a nucleus of either lucky or experienced individuals which manage to stay alive and carry on the bad work.

52. The Multimammate Rat *(Plate XIV, 52)*

Rattus natalensis

Although many races of this creature exist in West Africa, they are all essentially the same animal. Except in one respect, it is the most ordinary creature you could wish to see, and consequently the most difficult to describe. The one unusual feature is the presence (in the female only, of course) of up to twelve pairs of teats, regularly spaced from the groin to the armpits. Five pairs is the normal maximum for rats and mice, so provided you have a female, you can always distinguish a Multimammate Rat. It is greyish brown in the young, reddish in the adult, with underparts of grey hairs tipped with white. The tail is about the same length as the head and body. Total length may be up to a foot.

The Multimammate Rat was originally a savannah mammal, but nowadays there are few areas in the High Forest to which it has not penetrated. The secret of its sucess is probably two-fold: first, it is a successful commensal, and finds Man's houses an attraction rather than a deterrent; second, it is bigger and stronger than its truly forest-dwelling rival, the Jumping Mouse, and has more offspring at a birth. I have recorded up to fifteen. It will nest almost anywhere, including in drawers and bookshelves, and will use anything it can gnaw as nesting material. Like the Black Rat, it does thousands of pounds' worth of damage yearly, to growing crops, to stored food, and to household goods. Like the Black Rat, too, it could be largely kept down in houses if only West Africans would keep cats for this purpose.

53. The Jumping Mouse (*Plate XIV, 53*)

Rattus morio

The Jumping Mouse is the commonest *Rattus* and, indeed, the commonest Rodent of the High Forest zone. It is distinguished from most other rats and mice by its very short, soft fur. The upper parts are grey in the young, a beautiful warm red-brown in the adult. Beneath, it has the same grey, white-tipped fur as we find in the Multimammate Rat. The head and body measurement is about four and a half inches, the tail six inches. The weight, up to two ounces, is about half that of the Multimammate Rat.

This pretty little mouse occurs both in mature High Forest and in farms. Occasionally it enters houses. It is undoubtedly a pest. Like most forest mice, it rarely lives in holes, preferring the shelter of vegetation or dead logs, sometimes even hollow trees. It is a good climber. The name comes from its marked ability to leap in a vertical direction.

Two to four only seems to be the normal number of young in a litter, but the species, like most *Rattus*, breeds almost throughout the year.

54. The Climbing Wood Mouse (*Plate XIV, 54*)

Rattus alleni

I have included this small mouse because when hollow trees are smoked to obtain dormice for the stew-pot, this is one of the creatures which is often the first to fall into the fire. It is almost exactly like the Jumping Mouse, but smaller (head and body, three and a half inches) and lighter (only half the weight). The ears and feet are relatively short, but the coloration is exactly the same as in the Jumping Mouse.

55. The Rufous Nile Rat or Kusu   (*Plate XV, 55*)
Arvicanthis niloticus rufinus

This is a medium-sized Rat, about six inches long with a six-inch tail. Its rather long, harsh, speckled fur gives the effect of a yellow-brown colour, which is tinged with red to a variable extent. Perhaps the easiest feature by which to recognise it is the rounded ears, not prominent but set very close to the head. It is a diurnal animal, living in grass more especially in the savannah zones, but also in the High Forest in clearings and cultivated areas. The colour and the length and unevenness of the fur help to conceal it, an important matter more particularly in animals which venture out in the daytime. It lives in burrows, and is a cereal-rather than a root-eater. Hence it is not such a pest as many of the savannah Rodents, for grass-seeds and fallen grains make up the bulk of the diet.

56. The Spotted Grass Mouse   (*Plate XV, 56*)
Lemniscomys striatus

This, and its relative the Barbary Mouse, are quite the prettiest of all mice. Despite its name, the Spotted Grass Mouse appears to be *striped* longitudinally with buff on a dark brown background. Actually, the stripes are made up of a series of *spots* which are placed very close together.

Its way of life is very like that of the Kusu just described. Doubtless its smaller size (about five inches) indicates a diet of smaller seeds, but it also is diurnal, seed-eating, and lives in burrows. I have also found insect remains in the stomach. It lives in Guinea Savannah, but has also penetrated the High Forest wherever there is grass, mainly in cultivated areas and along roadsides.

The Barbary Mouse is very like the Spotted Grass Mouse, but lives only in the savannah zones, and has true *stripes*.

57. The Three-striped Mouse (*Plate XV, 57*)

Hybomys trivirgatus

This and the One-striped Mouse (*H. univittatus*) are handsome little mice found throughout the High Forest zone, the Three-striped to the west and the One-striped to the east of the Niger. The body fur is a dusky olive colour, except the under-surface, which is buff. Down the middle of the back runs a black stripe. In the Three-striped species, this is supplemented by two further, rather fainter stripes, one on either side. The animal is about five inches long with a tail of the same length.

These mice remain on the ground, never climbing trees as do so many forest species. They move about in the daytime, feeding largely upon fallen fruits. Even when undisturbed they move in a series of rapid runs, each starting with a jump. The power for this jump comes from the very long hind legs and feet. It is surprising how effective this type of movement can be in deceiving the eye. Their coloration is admirably suited to escaping detection; even when one watches closely it is very difficult to follow their jerky passage. If there is no breeze, it is often easier to hear the creatures than to see them. Even their tiny teeth make quite a noise as they gnaw at fruits in the silence of the forest.

Among forest mice, these two species appear to be exceptional both in their coloration and in their diurnal activity. They do, however, conform to type in that they do not excavate holes for themselves. Fallen logs and rotting timber apparently provide all the shelter they need.

Three to five offspring are produced in a litter.

58. The Shaggy Rat (*Plates XV, 58*)

Dasymys incomtus

This is the nearest approach that we have in West Africa to a genuine Water Rat. It is about six inches long, with a tail the same length. As the name implies, the fur is very long, dark grey and tinged to a varying degree with yellow or some shade of brown.

It lives a very retiring life among reeds on and near water. Through the reeds it makes regular pathways, which take the form of tunnels among the dead and rotting vegetation. It nests in rather firmer places, usually on a tussock. Its food is thought to be young shoots and water plants. Two or four young are born in a litter. It is apparently not a pest of cultivation, though it may become so if swamp rice becomes a popular crop. It is found in High Forest occasionally, but appears to be commoner in Guinea Savannah. It takes to the water readily and swims well.

59. The Pygmy Mouse (*Plate XVI, 59*)
Mus minutoides

Pygmy Mice of various forms occur all over West Africa. They are immediately recognised by their very small size, commonly only two and a half inches, with a two-inch tail. Although they are not often caught, this is probably the fault of the trapping systems used, which are mostly designed for larger creatures. In fact it seems probable that they are extremely common. Like other members of the *Mus* group, they can live almost anywhere, in holes or in thick vegetation, even in houses. They will also eat almost anything their small teeth can tackle. Both vegetable matter and insects are taken. There are four or five young in a litter.

60. The Swamp Rat (*Plate XVI, 60*)
Malacomys longipes

The Latin name of this creature means 'long-footed soft-furred-mouse', which in itself is a very good description. About six inches long with an eight-inch tail, its main pecularities are indeed those mentioned in the name. The hind foot is in fact up to an inch and a half long, longer even than that of a Gerbil of similar size.

The Swamp Rat lives in damp places, not by any means always swamps, in the High Forest. It nests in the vegetation, and comes out at night to feed. It would seem that the long hind feet and tail are useful not in hopping as one might expect, but in sitting up on the squelchy earth or sodden vegetation while tackling a morsel of vegetable matter held in the forefeet. But we know very little about the creature's way of life otherwise.

61. The Rufous-bellied Rat *(Plate XVI, 61)*

Lophuromys sikapusi

This curious little rat is about five inches long with a tail of only two and a half inches. It is very dark reddish-brown above, lighter red below, and the fur is of very even length, remarkably stiff and sleek like sealskin. Like the last species, it is found in the High Forest, including areas under cultivation, and seems to show a preference for damp areas, though not actual swamps. Save that it is nocturnal and strictly a ground-dweller, we know little or nothing of its way of life. From the collector's point of view, it has one other peculiarity —it is remarkably hard to skin without mishap. The skin seems to be lacking in fibres, like that of a Cutting Grass or Porcupine, and is easily torn.

62. The Pouched Rat or Giant Rat *(Plate XVI, 62)*

Cricetomys gambianus

This enormous rat grows up to fifteen inches long, with an eighteen-inch tail, which has a characteristic white tip. The 'pouches', which give it one of its English names, are pockets of skin inside the cheeks, similar to those found in the monkeys. They are used to collect food which, instead of eating it on the spot, the animal carries away to its hole.

The Giant Rat is found in forest and savannah almost throughout Africa. It lives in burrows which are provided with several exit-holes. It can also support itself in the sewers and rubbish-dumps of large towns, where it does comparatively little damage, and on farms, where its status as a pest is in little doubt.

Unlike most Rodent pests, however, it is actively sought out and killed, smoke and dogs or traps being used. The meat is said to be good.

Like most of its relatives, the Giant Rat is nocturnal. Driving along the roads at night, one may often see it in the headlights of a car, pottering along a ditch or crossing the road. Its slow and unsteady-looking walk and the high carriage of the white-tipped tail make it rather a stupid-looking beast. The food gathered on its extensive nightly wanderings is mainly vegetable matter, picked up by chance from the ground. It does, however, make more deliberate and destructive journeys when the crops in neighbouring farms are ripe.

Even for a Rat, this species is very verminous. Apart from a normal complement of fleas, ticks and lice, it also carries a large cockroach-like parasite which is found on no other animal.

63. The Fat Mouse   (*Plate XVI, 63*)

Steatomys caurinus

This species and closely related forms probably occur all over West Africa in the savannah zones, though records are few and far between. It is easily recognised by the corpulence from which its name derives, and by the fact that the four- or five-inch body is followed by a tail only two inches long.

The Fat Mouse lives in burrows, coming out at night to feed on grass seeds and probably other small fruits, not excluding the occasional groundnut. The most remarkable feature of its biology, however, is that there is fairly conclusive evidence that the creature 'aestivates'. It seems that particularly thick layers of fat are laid down beneath the skin and round the gut during the rains and shortly after, when food is plentiful. When the dry season really becomes severe and food is short, it goes to sleep in its burrow, and lives on the stored fat.

This way of life is, of course, similar in effect to that of many northern mammals, which hibernate during the winter when food is scarce. In particular, it is reminiscent of the behaviour of the European Dormice. It is not surprising therefore that the natives of both regions have discovered that the two animals are, at the beginning of the period of sleep, exceptionally tasty morsels, roast or fried in their own fat.

OTHER RODENTS

64. The Crested Porcupine   (*Plate XVII, 64*)

Hystrix cristata

The Crested Porcupine is one of those few animals which occur in the Mediterranean region (including southern Europe) as well as in Africa south of the Sahara. In West Africa it is found in the High Forest and in both the savannah zones.

This is the largest of all African Rodents, and may weigh over half a hundredweight. It need hardly be said, therefore, that it is hunted for food. Man, however, is not its only enemy. Probably many of the Cats will kill young Porcupines, but the main natural enemies of the adult are the Leopard, Hunting Dog and other large creatures. Against the would-be attacker, the Crested Porcupine is better defended than any other Rodent. Indeed, unless it is taken completely by surprise and killed instantly, it is liable to turn attacker itself. Rattling the loose and hollow tail-quills, it will scuffle backwards towards the enemy; unless the latter is either very experienced or very quick, it is liable to get one or more of the large spines of the back lodged in its skin. Should a spine become firmly embedded, its barbed point works inwards, and may reach a vital spot and kill. The Porcupine itself sheds quills very

4* 57

easily, and may make its escape while its attacker is trying to get rid of a very large thorn in the flesh.

Porcupines live singly or in pairs, spending the day in the permanent shelter of rocky clefts, or in temporary shelters near their feeding grounds, such as Aard-vark burrows. At night they emerge to feed on roots, bark and other vegetable matter including crops.

Two to four young are born in a litter. They are striped black and white when very young.

65. The Brush-tailed Porcupine (*Plate XVII, 65*)
Atherurus africanus

About the size and build of the Cutting Grass, this is a really common High Forest species. As can be seen from the illustration, its spines are by no means the formidable affairs of the Crested Porcupine, but are probably a fairly effective defence against Civets and other small Carnivores which may attack it. The tail quills are, as in the larger species, used as a warning rattle.

The Brush-tailed Porcupine, apart from being an interesting creature about which we should like to know more, is also an unmitigated pest in forest farms. It may lie up under any fallen log or tree-root during the day, and emerge to wreak havoc on the farms at night. Though its teeth are not so powerful as those of the Cutting Grass, it is a good digger, and does most of the damage in root-crops. As with the Cutting Grass and the Crested Porcupine, traps with jaws are of little use, for the animal will chew its foot off if it is so caught. The most effective form of trap is certainly the noose, set in a very low palm-rib fence. The palm-ribs are placed so close together that the animal cannot get through. But at intervals a gap is

CRESTED PORCUPINE. *Twi:* kɔtɔkɔ. *Ewe:* dzirdza. *Dagbane:* ʃelnle. *Igbo:* ɛbi ogwu. *Yoruba:* ŏre alagbon *Hausa:* bĕguwa.

Plate XVII

64 Crested Porcupine   66 Cane Rat or Cutting Grass

65 Brush-tailed Porcupine   67 West African Mole Rat

Plate XVIII

68   African Civet   70   Two-spotted Palm Civet

69   Genet

Plate XIX

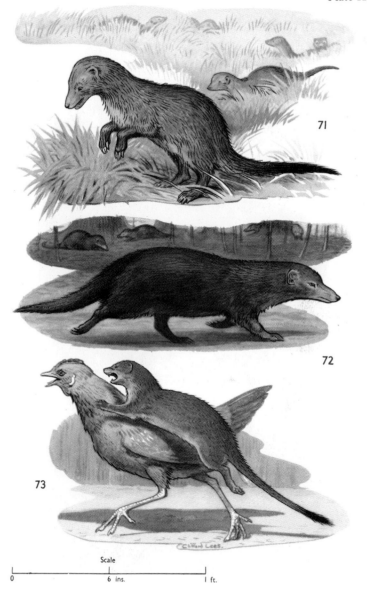

71   Gambian Mongoose

72   Cusimanse or Long-nosed Mongoose

73   Dwarf Mongoose

Plate XX

76

74

75

Scale

0 ⊢———————————⊣ 1 fr.

74 Marsh Mongoose   76 Egyptian Mongoose

75 White-tailed Mongoose

deliberately left, and in each gap is placed a wire noose. The Porcupine trots along the fence till it finds the gap, and next morning the farmer finds his supper waiting for him. (The flesh, incidentally, is much like that of the Cutting Grass.)

It would seem that two to four young are born in a litter. They can be tamed very easily, and become most friendly and confiding, though scarcely decorative pets.

66. The Cane Rat or Cutting Grass   *(Plate XVII, 66)*

Thryonomys swinderianus

The Cutting Grass is a member of the Porcupine group of Rodents, but lacks spines. Well over a foot long, it is heavily built, with short legs and a short tail. It weighs up to sixteen pounds. The fur is coarse—brown, flecked with black, the underparts white. The big head bears enormous front teeth, much larger than those of the Brush-tailed Porcupine.

The Cutting Grass was originally no doubt an inhabitant of the savannah, particularly the Guinea Savannah. Today its range is extended right into the High Forest wherever there is cultivation and grass. The heavy front teeth deal efficiently with the coarsest grasses, as well as sugar cane, maize and Guinea corn. Even cassava sticks will suffice when there is nothing better to be had.

It hides by day in the vegetation. Like the Hare, it brings forth the young above ground, with their eyes open and their fur developed. The only birth I was privileged to witness produced six offspring. There are probably at least two litters a year. This fecundity explains why the Cutting Grass is able to survive the most organised persecution to which any West African mammal is subjected. It is hunted with dogs, with spears, with guns and dim headlamps, and with every conceivable kind of trap. If during the pursuit it swims a river, there are men in canoes to chase it again.

The assiduity which the West African displays in com-

59

passing the capture of this rather ugly creature is readily appreciated by anyone who has tasted the meat. It is superb.

67. The West African Mole Rat (*Plate XVII, 67*)
Cryptomys zechi

These little creatures are quite unique in West Africa. There is nothing else that looks remotely like them, or has a comparable way of life. About six inches long, stoutly built, and with a mere stump of a tail, they are covered in short, very soft fur of a pale pinkish-orange colour, with white marks on the forehead and crown. The feet and legs are remarkably short, and the former very broad. But it is the head which is most remarkable. It seems to be all front teeth, with stout whiskers, but no eyes or ears. In fact, the eyes are very much reduced, but present and to a certain extent effective, while the ears simply have no external flap, only the ear-hole being visible. The nose is remarkably broad.

Mole Rats live practically their whole lives beneath the soil, making very long feeding-burrows, and throwing up earth at intervals in little heaps. They live entirely on roots, both wild and cultivated. They frequent rather loose, preferably sandy soils, which they excavate partly with the feet, and partly by a 'bulldozer' action of the head.

It seems that only one young is normally born at a time.

When caught alive, they do little but grumble and fight, but it is possible to keep them in captivity. They seem to do quite well in a box of loose earth, with yam for food. Their water supply need not be supplemented, for they must get all their water from the food they eat.

CANE RAT or CUTTING GRASS. *Mende:* sewulo. *Twi:* akrante. *Ewe:* (e)xɔ. *Dagbane:* ŋɔŋle. *Igbo:* nci. *Yoruba:* ọya. *Hausa:* ɓēra.

LESSER CARNIVORES

The Carnivores include noble creatures such as the Lion and the Leopard, and familiar creatures such as the Cat and the Dog, but in this book I am going to describe only the Civet-Mongoose group, most members of which are well known to all West Africans, if only because they are frequently trapped and eaten.

The word Carnivore means eater of flesh, but that doesn't necessarily mean the type of flesh that we eat ourselves, nor does it mean that flesh is the only thing eaten. Generally speaking, the larger the Carnivore, the larger the prey. The smallest eat insects, lizards, snails and other small fry, the largest take antelopes and other big game. The 'true cats' such as Lion, Leopard, Wildcat and others are the most specialised, and feed almost entirely on fresh meat such as we ourselves would eat. They are the most active and deliberate hunters. But the Civet-Mongoose group are not nearly so particular about their diet. Their hunting depends less upon stalking and pouncing than upon chance encounters with small and weak animals. Some live partly on vegetable matter. Many are comparatively clumsy and ungainly looking. All have some kind of stink-gland. This stink-gland is used particularly by the solitary species, and a discharge from it is left as a 'trademark' on regular pathways. Presumably it helps the animal to find a mate.

The stink-gland has been used for thousands of years as an item of commerce. The smell is usually of a sickly-sweet nature, and forms the base for perfumes. By itself it would be revolting, but when a more astringent odour is superimposed (of flowers, for instance), the result obtained is generally considered most pleasing. Civets are the most important natural source of such perfume bases, or were until recently. The males can produce considerable quantities, and Civet farms were formerly established for the production both of the animal and of the scent.

CIVETS

68. The African Civet

(Plate XVIII, 68)

Viverra civetta

This is the largest of the Civet-Mongoose group, as big as most of the local dogs, though not so long in the leg. With its handsome spotted pelt, it should be a beautiful animal. But neither in its gait nor in its habits does it merit that adjective. Hunting, it snuffles and shuffles; eating, it gobbles and gorges.

Though nowhere very common, it is a well-known animal, and occurs throughout West Africa, in both forest and savannah. It is normally solitary in habits, the sexes meeting only to mate. It is nocturnal, and will eat almost anything. It is said to prey on the young of duikers and other small game, but anyone familiar with the creature can hardly imagine it catching anything that involved much running. Certainly it eats rodents, lizards, frogs, millipedes and snails. It will also take fallen fruits, and I have even found grass in its droppings. This was probably taken as a corrective for intestinal disorders, after the manner of dogs.

From two to four young are born in a litter, and, as is the case in the Insectivores, Bats and most Rodents, they are blind, naked and helpless at birth. In spite of the unprepossessing character of wild adults, and of many tame ones, the kittens are most charming pets. They are easily tamed (if that is the right word), and become absolutely fearless indoors. They growl at dogs, bite at bare ankles, sleep on the best cushions, or trot about the house clucking to themselves, on an endless search for something to eat. When overfed, they may even be affectionate for a short time.

CIVET. *Mende:* kewulɔ. *Twi:* ɔkankan. *Ewe:* dzogolo. *Dagbane:* zini. *Igbo:* ɛdi. *Yoruba.* ɛta. *Hausa:* jibda.

69. The Genets

(Plate XVIII, 69)

Genetta spp.

A number of Genets occur in West Africa. The commonest are the Forest Genet, *Genetta maculata*, and the Bush Genet, *G. tigrina*. In general, the former is found in the High Forest zone, the latter in the Guinea Savannah. Their ranges overlap considerably, however, and they are so alike in habits and in appearance, that they generally only bear a single native name.

Genets are very slender animals, about the same length as a domestic cat, but shorter in the leg and very much lighter in weight. The long, pointed head and the long palms and soles of the feet betray their relationship to the Mongooses, despite their rather cat-like appearance. The Forest Genet is boldly spotted very dark brown on a fawn background. The Bush Genet, rather a smaller animal, has more of a rusty tinge, and the spots are less distinct. Both have the typical stink-glands of the group.

Cat-like in appearance, they are also cat-like in habits. They are nocturnal, partly arboreal (the Forest Genet very much so), and essentially hunters, rather than mere scavengers like the Civet. They stalk their prey and pounce on it in very much the same way as a true Cat. They even have a mewing, cat-like utterance, and purr when fondled.

Up to six young may be born in a litter. Like the African and Palm Civets, they are easy to rear in captivity, and are often tame and tractable till almost fully grown. They are graceful even when young, but they do share with their relatives a delight in eating too much, which may prove fatal.

GENET. *Mende:* pewe. *Twi:* anemefaa. *Ewe:* abee. *Dagbane:* pɛyna. *Igbo:* ɛdi. *Hausa:* (i)nyāwara.

70. The Two-spotted Palm Civet   (*Plate XVIII, 70*)
Nandinia binotata

Restricted to the High Forest zone, and to fringing forest in the Guinea Savannah, the Palm Civet is the most arboreal of all West African Carnivores. It is rather longer and more heavily built than the Genets, with a very much longer, bushy tail. The ground colour of the fur is fawn or light brown, with numerous dark reddish-brown spots. The 'two spots' referred to in the name are whitish marks above the shoulder-blade, very small and rather inconspicuous on the live animal, but always quite obvious on a skin.

Like the Genets, the Palm Civet is strictly nocturnal, and spends the day curled up asleep in thick foliage. Its deliberate, prowling movements in the branches suggest that here is a Carnivore of great strength and cunning. In fact, this is far from the truth. It lives largely on fruits, being inordinately fond of banana and pawpaw which it steals from the farms, though it will also take mice and small birds. It has even been known to climb down a string from which a zoologist's collection of skulls and skeletons were hanging to dry, and gnaw the flesh and bones.

The call, possibly a mating cry, is a long-drawn-out 'yowl'. I have observed a pair at night, by bright moonlight, positively gambolling in the branches of a tall tree, possibly as a prelude to mating.

The kittens are most attractive, fluffy creatures. On the ground, they are most amusing with their clumsy, bundling way of going about. As is usual in this group, they over-eat.

PALM CIVET. *Mende:* ndandakulɔ. *Twi:* aberɛbeɛ. *Ewe:* ewɔɛ. *Dagbane:* gyaŋkumbuŋ. *Igbo:* ɛdi.

MONGOOSES

71. The Gambian Mongoose (Plate XIX, 71)

Mungos gambianus

This little mongoose will serve well as an introduction to the whole Mongoose section. None of these creatures can be called graceful or handsome. They suffer in appearance as compared with the Civet section in having small ears, laid close to the side of the head, and in lacking any attractive markings on the fur.

The Gambian Mongoose grows to about fourteen inches long, with a seven-inch tail. It has coarse, rather long grey fur with darker hairs mixed with the lighter ones. It is found throughout the western savannah, but is commoner in the Guinea Savannah zone, where it is easily the most abundant Carnivore.

Like many Mongooses, it hunts by day. Large parties of up to 25 animals may be encountered together. Undoubtedly communal hunting is as profitable as is the same system used by African tribes without firearms. In the case of the Mongoose, the prey is generally lizards, diurnal mice and insects, small but comparatively nimble creatures. A lone Mongoose would have little chance of hunting such creatures successfully. In the case of Man, Cane Rats and Duikers are the prey, and the same situation holds. Success in the form of a kill is usually due to the prey fleeing from one of the hunters and running into the claws and mouth (or spear or stick) of another.

While the pack is moving through thicker cover, they make a twittering sound, which clearly helps them to keep together. Troops of monkeys and of many other social mammals and birds are held together in much the same way.

MONGOOSE. Particular species—*M.:* pekulɔ (*Gambian*), hagbe (*marsh*). *T.:* ahweaa (*Gambian*), odompo (*marsh*), kɔkɔbo (*dwarf*). *E.:* yegbi. ewegbahi, dompo (*marsh*), kɔkɔbo (*dwarf*). *D.:* tubeya. *I.:* ufu. *Y.:* kɔlɔkɔlɔ (*dwarf*). *H.:* tunku, wāzāgi (*white tailed*).

72. The Cusimanse or Long-nosed Mongoose

Mungos obscurus *(Plate XIX, 72)*

A small dark forest Mongoose, certainly the commonest in the High Forest zone, the Cusimanse is one of the best-known Carnivores in West Africa. It resembles the Gambian Mongoose in appearance, save that the fur is a very dark brown, and the nose is somewhat longer. In size it is similar.

In habits also, the Cusimanse is comparable to the Gambian Mongoose. Hunting by day, it moves in rather smaller parties (possibly only a single family, rather than two or three combined), and is sometimes met with singly. It is said that co-operative hunting has in this species reached quite a high pitch. The Giant Rat (easily as big as the Cusimanse) is driven from its hole by one member of the party, who goes down after it; then the others pounce as it emerges. Normally, however, its prey is much smaller fry. I have found mice, lizards, insects and earthworms in the stomachs of shot specimens.

This species is adept at climbing trees. Several times I have seen this performance when a dog was in the vicinity. Whether it ever hunts in the trees is not definitely known, but it seems doubtful. When not hunting, it normally rests on the ground, under a fallen log or thick vegetation.

It has an assortment of chirping and whistling calls. Often heard when the creature is hunting, they gain in volume and urgency when it is put to flight.

It is a most engaging pet, clean, endlessly inquisitive and quite fearless.

73. The Dwarf Mongoose *(Plate XIX, 73)*

Herpestes sanguineus

The Latin name of this tiny, slender Mongoose (it is about the size of a Ground Squirrel) refers to its ruddy colour, but it might equally well refer to its sanguinary habits. Living mainly in the Guinea Savannah, it also invades High Forest in cultivated areas, and spreads among the small birds and mammals a perfectly justifiable terror wherever it goes. Though it will take smaller prey such as insects, and even occasionally eat fruits, it is for its size a mighty hunter. Solitary in habits, it is quite quick and nimble enough to capture mice, small birds and lizards unaided. It has, moreover, an evil and well-earned reputation as a chicken-thief. I once caught one within twenty yards of a rest house, in a trap which contained a live mouse. It then escaped from the cage in which I deposited it, by biting through the wire. That evening it was found in the caretaker's fowl-house, where it had already slain two of the occupants. That was the end. To keep it as a pet would be asking for trouble.

74. The Marsh Mongoose (Plate XX, 74)

Atilax paludinosus

This is a large Mongoose, about eighteen inches long, with a thirteen-inch tail, and a handsome, almost uniform chocolate-brown pelt. It is solitary and nocturnal in habits. It is commonest in High Forest, but is said to occur in the savannah, wherever adequate cover and marshy ground are to be found. It feeds very largely upon crabs and frogs, paying nightly visits to favourite hunting-grounds. These may include ruts on roads as well as more natural streams, pools and swamps. It is nowhere very abundant.

The female has only two teats, and one assumes that not more than two young are born in a litter. If this is so, it is an unusually small number for a Carnivore.

75. The White-tailed Mongoose (Plate XX, 75)

Ichneumia albicauda

This species is somewhat larger even than the Marsh Mongoose, which it resembles in its nocturnal, solitary habits. It is found almost throughout Africa in the savannah zones. Its colour is rather dirty grey, with longish, coarse fur, and a

67

tail which is distinctly bushy and may be either white *or black* at the tip. It eats almost anything, including mammals, birds, reptiles, frogs, insects, snails and crabs. It also has something of a reputation with hunters for stealing drying meat in their camps at night. As in the Marsh Mongoose, litters of young are said to be small.

76. The Egyptian Mongoose (*Plate XX, 76*)

Herpestes ichneumon

About the size of the White-tailed Mongoose, this species has a much neater, speckled grey coat. It is diurnal, lives in the savannah, and hunts in small packs or in pairs. It is probably true to say that except for the Dwarf Mongoose, this is the most active hunter of all. It makes a good pet.